DIAGNOSTIC IMPLICATIONS OF SPEECH SOUNDS

The Reflections of Developmental Conflict and Trauma

DIAGNOSTIC IMPLICATIONS OF SPEECH SOUNDS

The Reflections of Developmental Conflict and Trauma

By

CLYDE L. ROUSEY, Ph.D.

Speech Pathologist, Menninger Foundation
Topeka, Kansas
Visiting Associate Professor in Speech Pathology
Kansas University
Lawrence, Kansas

and

ALICE E. MORIARTY, Ph.D.

Clinical Psychologist, Research Department
Menninger Foundation
Topeka, Kansas

With an Introduction by

PETER OSTWALD, M.D.

University of California School of Medicine
San Francisco, California

CHARLES C THOMAS • **PUBLISHER**
Springfield · *Illinois* · *U. S. A.*

Published and Distributed Throughout the World by
CHARLES C THOMAS • PUBLISHER
BANNERSTONE HOUSE
301-327 East Lawrence Avenue, Springfield, Illinois, U.S.A.
NATCHEZ PLANTATION HOUSE
735 North Atlantic Boulevard, Fort Lauderdale, Florida, U.S.A.

*With THOMAS BOOKS careful attention is given to all details of
manufacturing and design. It is the Publisher's desire to present books
that are satisfactory as to their physical qualities and artistic possibilities
and appropriate for their particular use. THOMAS BOOKS will be true
to those laws of quality that assure a good name and good will.*

Preface

THE LONGTERM studies of normal children carried on at the Menninger Foundation by Dr. Lois B. Murphy, Dr. Alice E. Moriarty, and others, have been concerned with global aspects of growth and development and with ways in which children deal with vicissitudes of growth. One aspect of these processes was the way in which children communicated verbally.

Observations of thirty-two normal preschool children in 1954 alerted us to the fact that speech is likely to be an especially vulnerable area, since half of the sample characteristically used faulty articulation. Other children were known to deviate from generally accepted standards of voice quality or rhythm. Furthermore, when these preschoolers were pressured by the need to relate to unfamiliar people or to deal with objects or test demands which were difficult, speech seemed to deteriorate more than motor functioning. We reasoned that speech might be especially vulnerable since it was only newly acquired or still in the process of becoming established. Although we did not equate good speech with good adjustment, it occurred to us that poor or deviant speech might be a particularly sensitive indicator of problems in adjustment.

This thinking was advanced when a speech pathologist (Dr. Rousey) joined the research staff. His formal examination of the speech and hearing of twenty-four prepuberty-aged children made even more impressive the vulnerability of the speech area since eighteen children (75%) then exhibited deviant speech to a degree serious enough to interfere at least mildly with the child's capacity to communicate with others. We felt that it might be possible to relate specific distortions in the production of speech sounds or in the auditory reception of speech sounds to dynamic factors such as aggressive or sexual drives and patterns of interpersonal relationships. These probable relationships were then expressed in terms of a series of hypotheses devised by Rousey. After assessing the sound misusages, Rousey postdicted various aspects of repression or denial of sexuality, expression of aggressive impulses, maintenance

[v]

of infantile forms of relating, withdrawal and lack of trust in others, chronic anxiety, capacity for impulse control, adequacy of mother-child and father-child relationships, control of anger and gross indicators of neurological malfunctioning.

The validity of these postdictions was gauged by Moriarty's review of psychiatric and other data which had been collected on the sample since infancy. The fact that 83 per cent of the 233 postdictions were judged to be accurate, with only eighteen post-dictions inaccurate and twenty-two not verifiable, suggested the usefulness of viewing speech projectively to assess a number of areas of child functioning.

Following a review of classical theories of speech and language, the authors have described the theoretical background and develop-ment of the specific hypotheses and presented examples of the validating process. Although the hypotheses were formulated by Rousey and validated by Moriarty's assessment of other clinical data, both authors take responsibility for the presentation and discussion of the findings. We feel that our system of analyzing sound deviations in an individual's use of speech and hearing provides a new diagnostic tool for the psychological assessment of several aspects of human functioning.

We are grateful for the helpful suggestions of our colleagues at the Menninger Foundation and the University of Kansas, for the facilities made available by these institutions, and for the grants which made the study possible. Special appreciation is felt for the encouragement and specific help of Doctors Gardner Murphy, Lois Murphy, Martin Mayman, Cotter Hirschberg, Povl Toussieng and Paul Pruyser.

Collaboration of the two authors was made possible by support from USPHS Grant No. M-4093, by the Gustavus and Louise Pfeiffer Foundation and the Menninger Foundation. Dr. Rousey participated in the study as a Special Research Fellow under USPHS Grant MF 17580.

C. L. R.
A. E. M.

Introduction

You ARE ABOUT to read a remarkable book dealing with one of the most basic clinical aspects of acoustic communications: *The Diagnostic Implications of Speech Sounds*. Physicians, psychologists, and linguists have been interested in this subject for many years. Physicians rely heavily upon spoken communication as the only way in which a patient can reveal himself, describe his symptoms, trace the history of his problems, and verbally express his suffering. Psychologists use speech and verbal processes as the most important way to ascertain formal intelligence and, in more recent studies, to estimate the presence of anxiety, depression and other disturbing emotions. For linguists speech behavior provides a corpus from which understanding is derived about how the language code is organized and reproduced. These and other professional workers in the field of speech communication will welcome this study.

Dr. Clyde Rousey describes speech patterns and speech disturbances of twenty-four children and makes 233 statements about what these disturbances may imply in terms of the speakers' states of emotional maturity. These statements were checked by Dr. Alice Moriarty against the findings from clinical examinations conducted on these children by other staff members. Four out of five times Dr. Rousey correctly anticipates these findings. That's a terrific batting average! How did they do it?

First of all, I think that Dr. Rousey must have listened extremely well to each child. His are the ears of a highly trained, skillful, and sophisticated speech pathologist who attends not only to the referential properties of words but also to the way speech sounds are voiced and articulated. Like a composer who spots each instrument within the rich fabric of orchestral sound, Dr. Rousey can tell how the vocal cords, resonators, and mouth structures participate in making the total speech product. But there is much more to analytic listening than the use of one's ears. Dr. Rousey also spoke and interacted with each child subject. He looked and perhaps even touched in order to enrich his understanding of the phonologic processes. He tested a specific motor skill — diadochokinesis — to ascertain each child's neurologic integrity. Finally, I think some of the success of this project can be attributed to the way Drs. Rousey and Moriarty were able to share their assumptions about the meaning of terms like "oral deprivation," "sexual identification," "passive-aggressive tendencies," and other concepts descriptive of emotional maturation and immaturity. Without such mutual understanding of difficult behavioral concepts, the investigators would most likely have come up with the kinds of data one gets when untrained listeners respond to tape-recorded replicas of complex communicative behavior. One of the great advantages of the Rousey-Moriarty project is that it does not purchase objectivity at the cost of superficiality.

It now is necessary for those of us in psychiatry, speech, psychology, and other clinical fields to refine the maturational concepts used in this study and look for ever more useful relationships between them and specific patterns of speech behavior. To do this, we will probably need help from geneticists, acousticians, neurologists, linguists, and other specialists who can work out details at different levels of this complex problem. The rewards should be exhilarating. Not only may it one day be possible to answer the question "What built-in capacities of the human nervous system enable infants to learn speech?" but hopefully we will also learn to identify those specific social experiences which release or inhibit our native capacities for communication. Such knowledge should help ultimately to make us better therapists able to comprehend quickly what ails the patient with a communication problem and to remedy it more effectively. This is one of the practical benefits to be gained from the kind of investigation which Drs. Rousey and Moriarty are about to present to us.

PETER OSTWALD, M.D.
University of California School of Medicine
San Francisco, California

Contents

[ix]

DIAGNOSTIC IMPLICATIONS OF SPEECH SOUNDS

The Reflections of Developmental Conflict and Trauma

Chapter I

Introduction

THIS REPORT proposes a new method of analyzing the sounds used in speech and hearing and of relating these findings to the evaluation of personality development and mental health, whether under research conditions or in a clinical setting. The purpose of the present report is to present a theoretical formulation of the meanings which may be associated with the sounds used in verbal language and to evaluate clinically postdictions of early developmental experiences, difficulties and conflicts. These postdictions were arrived at by integrating material gathered in a speech evaluation within a new theoretical system. They were evaluated in reference to extensive developmental data accumulated on a group of "normal"* children who have been examined and observed at the Menninger Foundation in a series of studies beginning in infancy.

While we cannot review these studies in detail here, a brief summary of their nature and focus will provide the readers with an understanding of the background in which the present hypotheses were fostered and explored.

In 1947, Sibylle Escalona and Mary Leitch designed and carried on a study entitled, *Early Phases of Personality Development: A Non-normative Study of Infancy Behavior* (23). Various formal and informal methods utilized in their study produced detailed descriptions of the infants and their families, their interactions, and the expressive patterns of infants and their mothers.

In 1953, thirty-one children from the original sample of 128 infants were selected as subjects for study of coping patterns in preschool children under the direction of Lois B. Murphy. This

---

*Our use of the term "normal" refers to the fact that the infancy sample was chosen as free of obvious physical or mental defect. Subsequently the sample maintained this normality insofar as no child was delinquent or showed signs of gross mental illness. It did not rule out the presence of problems in many areas.

was followed by a study of development in the latency years; then by a third study at prepuberty focusing on the maintenance of mental health. In the course of this sequence of studies,[1] thorough pediatric, psychological, and psychiatric examinations of the children were made along with observations of the subjects in a variety of situations and repeated interviews of the mothers. An important part of each of these studies was an effort to understand patterns of self-expression and communication.

The opportunity to explore communication in greater detail became possible when the senior author came to the Menninger Foundation for postdoctoral research training. This meshing of interests, along with further observations of psychiatric patients, earlier preliminary consideration of the psychological meaning of sounds by one of the authors (Bradford and Rousey, 1961; Mayman and Rousey, 1963), and thinking activated by the reading of Moses's book, *The Voice of Neurosis* (1954), led to the formulation of a series of hypotheses relating psychological behavior and the use of sound.

Though clinicians have stressed the meaningfulness of the content of the words their patients use, the potential diagnostic clues in the processes of speaking and hearing sounds have received little emphasis in the usual psychological evaluation. In other words, little significance has been attached to the constituents of the words, that is vowels and consonants. This diagnostic oversight or failure to

---

[1]Some results of this series of studies have been presented in books, monographs, journal reports and in talks at professional meetings. The following publications are particularly relevant to the current study: Escalona, S., and Heider G.: *Prediction and Outcome.* New York, Basic Books, 1959. Moriarty, A. E.: Coping patterns of preschool children in response to intelligence test demands.. *Genetic Psychology Monographs, 64*:3-127, 1961. Escalona, S., and Moriarty, A. E.: Prediction of school age intelligence from infant tests. *Child Development, 32*:597-605, 1961. Murphy, L.B.: Preventive implications of development in the preschool years. Chapter 10 in *Prevention of Mental Disorders in Children.* Gerald Caplan, ed., New York, Basic Books, 1961. Murphy, L. B., and Collaborators: *The Widening World of Childhood.* New York, Basic Books, 1962. Murphy, L.B., Moriarty, A. E., and Raine, W.: *Development and Adaptation* (In preparation). Heider, G.: Vulnerability in infants and young children. Monograph in press in *Genetic Psychology Monographs.* Moriarty, A. E.: I.Q. Constancy and I.Q. Change; a Clinical View of Relationships Between Tested Intelligence and Personality (to be published).

All names of children used in this book are pseudonyms. However, they are the same children as referred to in the above noted publications.

consider the implications of the use of sound by clinicians and by experimentalists as well was understandable, yet peculiar. It probably reflected professional rejection on the part of psychologists and psychiatrists of elements thought to be of primary value and interest to phoneticians. Yet, this viewpoint neglected remarks by Wundt (1900), Freud (1901), and Sapir (1926), calling attention to the potential psychical meanings implied not only by words but also by sounds. Although Freud's ideas on the meanings of slips of the tongue as applied to words became popular, his indirect suggestion of the psychological significance of an individual's misuse of sound never had serious consideration.

In the present setting, it was possible to explore in a rigorous manner the psychological dimensions involved in a child's use and misuse of sounds. Using the wealth of data collected on these children in the preceding years, the authors were able to assess the validity of postdictive statements made about the psychological functioning of the children on the basis of an hour-long speech and hearing examination. Although we realized that other interactional cues played a role in the synthesis of these impressions, we attempted to make inferences about the psychological status of the individual in his environment solely on the basis of the way the child reacted to and used sound.

In the following chapters we shall summarize theories about the development of sound and language and current thought concerning the use of sound, describe our rationale for postdicting relationships between social-psychological dimensions and use of sound and discuss the validity of these postdictions. While we are aware of methodological limitations such as the relatively small sample and the fact that one of the authors made judgments as to the accuracy of the postdictions, it is our belief that the usefulness of the exploratory ideas advanced in this pilot study will outweigh the shortcomings. Furthermore, we hope that this study will stimulate other scientists to undertake a searching and unbiased evaluation of the hypotheses proposed.

Chapter II

Theories About the Development and Uses of Speech and Language

The Relation Between Speech and Language

IN SEEKING to understand the reasons for the relative inattention to psychological aspects of sound as used in human verbal communication, it is first necessary to clarify past and present terminology and theory used in discussing sound. At the outset, it should be pointed out that most psychological writers have treated verbal communication rather globally, as opposed to a conceptualization emphasizing the specific patterns and qualities of sounds which occur in human language. Furthermore, the terms speech and language have been used interchangeably by many writers. For example, many psychological writers, in speaking of an analysis of a patient's speech, actually have referred to the *content* of the language used by their patients. For purposes of the present discussion, we shall differentiate between speech and language as follows:

> *Speech* is meant to refer to the sounds or, as they are technically termed, phonemes, which when used together in certain accepted ways then produce verbal language. *Verbal language* refers to the symbolic meanings attached to these sound groupings.[2]

Conceptual differences arising from the use of these definitions and the common interchange of these terms by many writers can be illustrated by reference to recent publications by psychologists and linguists. For example, a topic which has attracted increasing interest has been that which most writers refer to as *disruption in speech* as a result of anxiety. This subject unquestionably received its impetus as a result of the major research work completed by George Mahl (1956, 1959a, 1959b, 1960).

Other studies by Dibner (1956), Gleser, Gottschalk, and Springer

---

[2]Rousey and Toussieng (104), p. 4.

(1961), Krause (1961), Boomer and Goodrich (1961) and Matarazzo, Hess and Saslow (1962) have all focused on aspects of this problem. Feldman (1959) in commenting on expressions patients use from our standpoint also erroneously combines the different concepts of speech and language. However, in all of these authors' published reports, there was either an inferred or actual interchangeable use of the terms speech and language to refer to what we have defined more specifically as language.

There have been some exceptions to this joint use of the terms of speech and language. For example, linguists, psychiatrists, and laryngologists such as Moses (1954), Pittenger and Smith (1957), Pittenger, Hockett and Danehy (1960), and Ostwald (1959, 1961, 1963) presented proposals and research suggesting that the manner in which sounds are made is related to the psychological process which unfolds during an interview.

A frame of reference equating speech and language was probably inevitable in the thinking of modern day psychological investigators since philosophers and linguists have for centuries written about the origin of speech. From our viewpoint, they have really been concerned with the origin of language. A review of the major theories, both ancient and modern, will emphasize this point.

Ancient thinkers held that language is a divinely imparted gift, occurring with the creation of man. This was an encapsulated concept since it precluded the need for any other explanatory concepts. Other writers advanced theories similar to the divine theory in the sense that acceptance of the theory left no room for discussion. A significant step forward in theorizing was made by Plato (translated by B. Jowett, (1952). In *Cratylus,* he took the position that names:

> "are natural and not conventional; not a portion of the human
> voice which men agree to use; that there is a truth or correctness
> in them, which is the same for Hellenes as for barbarians."[3]

In the discussion which ensued in *Cratylus,* Socrates suggested that culture may have an influence on sounds.

Socrates' statement significantly advanced theorizing on the origin of language and later theorists of the origin of language based some

---

[3]Plato (translated by B. Jowett), (97), p. 85.

of their ideas on the concepts advanced in *Cratylus*. For example, more recent theorists have tended to view the onset of language as the result of either internal or external factors.

The chief proponent of internal factors was Müller (1891), who held that man had within him certain typical sounds which under sufficient stimulation are wrung out of him like the ringing of a bell by striking it. Counted on the other side of the question are men such as Smith (1804), Von Herder (cited in Müller, 1891), and DeLaguna (1923). In essence, these writers contended that the auditory environment which surrounds man is primarily responsible for evoking language. Somewhat outside this dichotomy of thinking about the origin of language was the thinking of another group who maintained that the development of oral language is related to gestures and expressive movements. Included in this group were Wundt (1907), Jesperson (1922), Paget (1930), Bloomfield (1914).

Of course, there have been writers who postulated that there is in man an interaction between external and internal processes which influences the development of language. Socrates, as noted above, was described by Plato as having thought that culture also influenced use of language symbols. Whitney (1868) suggested a joint interaction between external and internal factors in terms of language development. A recent statement of this viewpoint was made by Simon:

> ". . . in harmony with present biological and psychological knowledge, the development of speech in the race is best understood as 'learning,' occurring within a total configuration involving an internal energy system and an external energy system—each as a part of the whole."[4]

This brief review reflects the primary concern of theoreticians with the origin of language rather than with the meanings individual sounds may intrinsically have, or may come to acquire.

The idea that the use of sound may be of behavioral significance is perhaps new or unfamiliar to many readers since professional and lay people have usually attributed interest in speech sounds only to

---

[4]Simon (114), p. 17.

the elocutionists. This interest was eloquently presented in Shaw's *Pygmalion*. However, in the United States within the past thirty years, a professional group known as The American Speech and Hearing Association has devoted itself to study, diagnosis, and rehabilitation of persons having problems in the use of verbal communication. With reference to the specific category of speech as we have defined it, a perusal of the journal articles and books published by members of the association strongly suggested that most "authorities" have one of two viewpoints: either that (1) misuse of sound occurs when some organic predisposition or weakness leads to deviant speech and hearing behavior; or that (2) misuse of sound occurs when there is disruption in the broadly conceived process of learning which accompanies maturation (cf. Van Riper 1954, Curtis 1956, Berry and Eisenson 1956, Powers 1957, and Van Riper and Irwin 1958).

Of course, the preceding statement oversimplifies complex and sophisticated statements of these viewpoints. Only a few publications by members of the American Speech and Hearing Association have asserted that personality factors may be important determinants in the use and misuse of sounds. Even in publications utilizing such an explanation, usually only the phenomenon of stuttering is discussed (cf. Travis 1957, Murphy 1960, and Glauber 1958.

A clarification of the general viewpoint of many speech pathologists regarding the reason for the misuse of specific sounds hopefully will emphasize for the reader the difference between this viewpoint and our theoretical formulation which will be presented later in this report. In so doing, we are not discussing the validity of the ideas which are reviewed, but rather we are trying to set the stage for a later demonstration that equally attractive theoretical alternatives may be possible.

Speech pathologists have discussed the use of sounds under the general heading of articulation. Articulation may be defined as the acoustic result of certain physiological movements of the speech apparatus. Various terms have been used in the literature to designate problems in articulation. For example, one of the early American writers on this problem (Scripture, 1923) referred to articulation problems as lisping. Currently, the term lisping is used to designate a particular type of difficulty in using sounds. At least two types (i.e., frontal and lateral) of lisping are used for diagnostic purposes. Frontal lisping indicates the substitution of the th sound (as in ba*th*) for the s sound in words like *s*it or *c*ity. Lateral lisping refers to the sound produced by air spilling out into the buccal cavity through the molars whenever the s sound is produced. Although Scripture believed that most lisping problems were functions of poor habits and/or organic deficiencies, he also felt that there was lisping of neurotic origin. His comments on what he called neurotic lisping were as follows:

> "Neurotic lisping is allied to stuttering in its causation (fright, nervous strain) and in the presence of an emotional disturbance. It differs in having excessive muscular tension of a constant rather than a spasmodic kind; this results in speech somewhat like lisping and not in the peculiar sounds of the stutterer . . . The general treatment is mainly that for neurasthenia. General hygiene, mode of life (school, professional), oral habits, eye strain, nose and throat conditions, etc., must be considered. Arsenic, quinine, strychnine and other tonics, cold rubs, luke warm or cold half-baths, sprays, moist packs, electro-therapy, massage, change of climate, and sea baths may be tried. Open-air exercise is always admirable. Hypnotism and other forms of psychotherapy are often most efficient."[5]

In Travis' now classic volume on speech pathology (1931), articulation disorders were thought to be related to central and peripheral organic deficiencies. Orton's (1937) book, still widely quoted in many modern pediatric texts (Ford 1948, Nelson 1954), also emphasized the organic aspect of articulation problems. Neurologists (Wechsler 1963, Grinker and Bucy 1949, Neilsen 1955, and Wilson and Bruce 1955) generally promulgated the view that articulatory disorders are related solely to organic factors. For example, Brain[6] (1961), while giving lip service to the concept that abnormalities of speech are caused by other than neurological factors, omitted any detailed discussion of this possibility in his recent book. As we understand him, he dealt with the problem of misused sounds under the category of dysarthria. Furthermore, he seemed to exclude the

---

[5]Scripture (110), p. 185.
[6]Brain (10), p. 134.

possibility of psychological factors affecting the articulation of sounds in his discussion of dysarthria:

> "Dysarthria is a disorder of articulation which therefore does not involve any disturbance in the proper construction and use of words. In the dysarthric patients, symbolic verbal formulation is normal; only the mechanism of verbal sound production is affected."[7]

Many modern day speech pathologists are attached theoretically either to the organic viewpoint as espoused by neurologists or to a modification of an organic etiology as a result of learning. A brief review of the more popular textbooks in speech pathology will illustrate these points.

Probably one of the most influential writers on the problem of articulatory defects has been Charles Van Riper. In his standard text (1954), Van Riper discussed causes of articulation disorders under the headings of developmental influences, emotional conflicts, motor incoordination, organic abnormalities, and perceptual deficiencies. The majority of these headings were subsumed in the broad heading of organic deviations. Under the topic of emotional conflicts, he suggested that a lisp may in some cases have psychological determinants. However, he summarized his final viewpoint as follows:

> "In our opinion it is in this area (i.e., perceptual deficiencies) that most of the causes of articulation defects occur, but we have to admit that most of the research does not support that opinion."[8]

He went on to amplify this feeling further as he stated:

> "Despite the general negative tone of these research findings, most clinicians feel that their articulatory cases need a great amount of training in auditory perception in sensing the location of focal articulation points, in feeling where the tongue is and what it is doing."[9]

This is the basic viewpoint held by many modern speech pathologists. Van Riper's reference to perception seems to come close to,

---

[7]Brain (10), p. 108.
[8]Van Riper (128), p. 185.
[9]Van Riper (128), p. 185.

but from our viewpoint misses, one of the most important factors in the creation of an articulation problem. The missing factor in the causation of articulation problems is succinctly identified by the following statement which appeared in a paper by Klein and Schlesinger (1949):

> "In the careful research on seeing, hearing, feeling, the see-er, the hearer, the feeler are somehow obscured or lost. The *person him-self* (our italics), the pivot of all these sensations, the source and root of motives whose influences are sought, is ignored as a determinant of his own perceptual behavior"[10]

A later book by Van Riper and Irwin (1958) amplified some of Van Riper's earlier statements, presenting the problem within the context of learning. Their viewpoint was expressed clearly in the following passage taken from the preface to their book:

> "We are certain that speech is learned behavior and that it is monitored largely through automatic control systems."[11]

Another book, by Berry and Eisenson (1956), though acknowledging the possibility of adolescent or adult neurotic need for defective articulation, apparently assumed that the cause of the articulation problem could be treated by training the child to increase his auditory discrimination and his awareness of his error. Again, the emphasis seemed to be largely on perceptual deficiencies (organic factors) and a breakdown in learning. Milisen (1954) held much the same view as many of the above-mentioned authors. He stated that "defective articulation, a substitute response for normal articulation, results from the disruption of the normal learning process."[12]

One of the most recent texts for use by speech pathologists by Johnson, Darley, and Spriestersbach (1963) seems to completely omit consideration of the possibility of a psychological origin for articulation defects. Advising students training in speech pathology, they stated:

> "If a speaker's articulation problem warrants clinical attention, you will try to determine its causes. Your investigation will cover

---

[10]Klein and Schlesinger (57), p. 32.
[11]Van Riper and Irwin (129), p. 1. (No particular school of learning was emphasized and the word probably implied learning in a general and popular way).
[12]Milisen (70), p. 6.

the structural and physiological adequacy of the person's oral speech mechanism (Chapter 5), his intelligence (Chapter 10), his hearing acuity (Chapter 10), the amount and type of speech stimulation he has received, and the adequacy of his speech (Chapter 2)."[13]

A comprehensive application of learning theory to the problem of articulation disorders, under preparation by Winitz (1963), contends that articulation disorders occur when parents reinforce this incorrect behavior. In addition, Winitz demonstrated that it is possible to induce articulation substitutions in individuals by principles of operant conditioning. One of the problems inherent in Winitz's viewpoint may be understood by consideration of Orne's papers (1959, 1962) on how the demand characteristics of an experiment influence the actions of the subject. Orne suggested that the subject's wish to please the experimenter may influence the results which an experimenter obtains. Thus, the subject's relationship to the experimenter may be most important in the operant conditioning process. This aspect of how sound serves as a way of relating on different psychological levels underlies much of the rationale for the theoretical formulation of the present report.

None of these foregoing publications gave primary consideration to the possibility that misused sounds are psychologically and symbolically meaningful in the behavior of the person misusing them. However, some of the writers quoted above have secondarily suggested the possible impact of emotional factors on articulation problems. Van Riper and Irwin (1958) provided the most comprehensive current review of this possibility. They cited several references, but since some of these references were not available to this reviewer, they will be summarized as they were reviewed by Van Riper and Irwin. For example, Blanton and Blanton (1920) and Brown (1936), believed that an understanding of the emotional life of the child is of major importance in understanding the speech behavior. Searl (1936) was quoted by Van Riper and Irwin as attributing some of the errors of speech to "fixations at an earlier level of oral satisfaction."[14] After Van Riper and Irwin reviewed

---

[13]Johnson, Darley, and Spriestersbach (55), p. 96.
[14]Van Riper and Irwin (129), p. 41.

these articles, and several others to be reported shortly, they concluded that:

> "Probably the wisest course would be to table the question and withhold judgment (with reference to the influence of emotional factors) . . . We must never forget that both correct and incorrect pronunciation are products of learning."[15]

Irwin's later writing (1960) on the psychological implications of voice and articulation problems failed to deviate from his earlier position in collaboration with Van Riper (cf Van Riper and Irwin, 1958).

Van Riper on occasion (1954) has expressed in writing his conviction about the emotional significance which may become attached to articulation disorders. In his standard textbook on speech disorders, he stated very clearly, "The desire to remain a child or to return to childhood security has produced many symptoms of articulation disorders."[16] He also commented on the importance of speech sounds as a basis for relationships with others.

A review of the other research cited by Van Riper and Irwin (1958) as dealing with the psychological aspects of articulation disorders seems to contraindicate the rather presumptive tabling of the question of the influence of emotional factors on articulation problems. For example, Henry and Henry (1940) reported speech disturbances among Pilaga Indians, noting "that individuals with serious personality disturbances also have speech disturbances."[17] Furthermore, these authors reported that "although all Pilaga Indians talk some baby talk up to the age of seven, the most serious speech defects appear only in half or full orphans."[18] The sound disturbances as they appeared among the Pilaga Indian children seemed to suggest that the most serious speech defects developed where there was good reason to believe there was a poor emotional environment and an inability to establish relationships. This concept will be explored in more detail in the section of this report dealing with the formulation of our hypotheses and rationale.

---

[15]Van Riper (129), p. 109. (The phrase in parenthesis is ours.)
[16]Van Riper (128), p. 187.
[17]Henry and Henry (43), p. 362.
[18]Henry and Henry (43), p. 302.

The relationship between quality of articulation and ability to establish a relationship with people was further emphasized in an article by Rose (1943) who cited several case histories, among which were two boys with "dyslalic speech." These would probably be called articulation problems by the present writers. These children's chief emotional difficulty occurred in relating to others.

In a paper by Brodbeck and Irwin (1946), data were presented showing diminished sound usage in orphanage children during their first six months of life as compared with children of the same age living with their family. An explanation offered for this finding was that the orphanage children did not have the normal speech stimulation or relationships with a caring parent.

Wyatt's work (1949) on language development in childhood focused on the question of emotional factors affecting sound usage and misusage. Although Wyatt's work dealt only with the question of stammering and stuttering, she nevertheless made the point early in her work that learning to speak, like all other primary learning, would be influenced by the child's relationship to the mother. In other words, she emphasized the relationship factor necessary for the use of sounds. This concept was explored further by Wyatt and others (1962) with children having articulation problems. A recent study by Heinstein (1963) provided further evidence for considering mother-child interaction as a significant variable influencing use of sound. In a study of ninety-four children whose physical, mental and emotional development had been observed from birth to maturity, he found a greater incidence of difficulties with speech among children who were formula fed and whose mothers were characterized as cold by psychologists and social workers.

Speech pathologists have begun to consider specific ways in which psychological factors may be related to articulation problems. For example, McWilliams (1960) described the process of speech therapy with a six-year-old boy who was hospitalized when his parents were unable to cope with his frequent psychosomatic illnesses. He sustained difficulty with the *s* and *h* sounds, in general omitting them in his speaking. After a session wherein a connection between these sounds and an external feared stimulus was discovered, therapy seemed to progress more adequately. In conclusion she suggested:

"It becomes increasingly apparent that certain children may have psychologically determined speech symptoms and that these may well be the children who, after years of speech therapy, retain their symptoms in unaltered form."[19]

Solomon (1961), after studying personality and behavior patterns of children with functional defects of articulation, concluded:

". . . speech problems of this type, apparently, are not isolated phenomena but part of a total adjustive pattern. It is suggested that an underlying stress may be common to the diverse symptomatology here presented and that the infantile and nonassertive behavior could very well serve as anxiety-reducing devices to meet environmental pressure."[20]

Finally, this review comes to the writings of Moses (1954), a laryngologist who offered more specific hypotheses regarding the development of persistent speech problems. The unenthusiastic reception accorded his publications by many professional people was unfortunate since he pointed out in an essentially clinical style some of the psychological meaning which may become attached to sounds. For example, with regard to the phenomenon of lisping he wrote:

"Lisping at this age (he probably refers to early childhood, although he gives no specific ages) is a simple continuation of infantile oral gratification. Playing with saliva, touching mucous membranes with the tongue are among the earliest sources of pleasure. Children like to lisp because it involves a similar kind of enjoyment."[21]

Moses was also interested in aspects of speech other than the consonant sounds. Indeed, a major portion of his book was devoted to what he broadly labeled "voice." Recognizing the slow progress in research relating voice to personality, Moses wrote, "little has been accomplished . . . in a study of voice as a key to personality: normal, neurotic, or psychotic."[22]

Recent Research

Recently there have been attempts to explore the dimensions

---

[19]McWilliams (67), pp. 90-91.
[20]Soloman (116), p. 736.
[21]Moses (75), p. 23. (The comment in parenthesis is ours.)
[22]Moses (75), p. 7.

and uses of the human voice. For example, an article by Starkweather (1961), a book by Ostwald (1963), and a book edited by Davitz (1963) explored this question. The logical extension of their work to predict unknown psychological dimensions has not been made, perhaps because most research on the human voice has conceived of voice primarily as a mediator. Holzman (1963) suggested that the voice conceals as well as mediates dimensions of personality. Research underway by Holzman, Rousey, Schloesser, and Snyder (1963) is exploring Holzman's concept in depth.

In view of these recent studies, it is important to note that Sapir (as early as 1925) suggested the need for research relating the sounds of speech to psychological factors. He wrote:

"One of the most interesting unwritten chapters in linguistic behavior is the expressively symbolic character of sounds, quite aside from what the words in which they occur mean in a referential sense. On the properly linguistic plane sounds have no meaning, yet if we are to interpret them psychologically we would find that there is a subtle, though fleeting, relation between the 'real' value of words and the unconscious symbolic value of sounds as actually produced by individuals."[23]

Approximately three years later (1929), Sapir published a study regarding the phonetic symbolism of vowels with reference to how they affected the estimation of size. When the vowel *a* (as in the German *Mann*) was placed between two consonants, Sapir noted that there was a strong tendency to consider the word so formed as indicating something larger than if the vowel *i* (as in the French word *fini*) were placed between the same consonants.

Sapir's research on phonetic symbolism was studied at a later date by Newman who concluded:

"The basis of phonetic symbolism is fundamentally objective. The symbolic scale is constellated in accordance with such mechanical factors as position of articulation, acoustic resonance, frequency, size of oral cavity, vocalic length, consonantal voicing and phonetic structure."[24]

---

[23]Sapir (106), p. 6.
[24]Newman (84), p. 75.

However, Bentley and Varon (1933) took issue with Sapir and Newman and concluded:

> "There seems to be insufficient evidence that these graded attributes of sound (noted by Newman) carry in their own right (so to say) a symbolic reference."[25]

Although these authors struggled with the possibility that sounds may have a cognitive meaning such as large or small, the possibility that an individual sound may have affective meaning was not considered.

The next major group of studies purporting to study phonetic symbolism concentrated on the symbolism of language forms. For example, Brown, Black, and Horowitz (1955), Maltzman, Morisett, and Brooks (1956), and Brockbill and Little (1957), studied the ability of subjects to equate words from different languages with which they were unfamiliar. Although Brown, Black, and Horwitz argued there may be some features of phonetic symbolism which have universal validity, the latter authors felt the results of their research to be contrary to the hypothesis of any universal phonetic symbolism. However, Jakobson (1960) in a book edited by Kaplan and Werner reintroduced the concept that certain sounds appear more often than would be expected by chance in certain concepts among the world's languages. For example he noted, "stops and nasals—briefly, consonants formed by complete oral closure—predominate in parental terms."[26] This again raised the question of universal phonetic symbolism, for instance in words denoting parents. Jakobson based his observations and other corroborating remarks on his survey of the various world language forms. Jakobson further noted that "—55 per cent of the words denoting mother and only 15 per cent of those denoting father belong to *m*, *n* and *ng* (this is the sound *ng* as in coming) consonant classes."[27] In explaining his view how symbolism may become attached to certain sounds with special reference to the m sound, Jakobson wrote:

> "Often the sucking activities of a child are accompanied by a slight nasal murmur, the only phonation which can be produced

---

[25]Bentley (2), p. 85 (First phrase in parenthesis is ours.)

[26]Jakobson (52), p. 127.

[27]Jakobson (52) (Comment in parentheses is ours.)

when the lips are pressed to the mother's breast or to the feeding bottle and the mouth is full. Later, this phonatory reaction to nursing is reproduced as an anticipatory signal at the mere sight of food and finally as a manifestation of discontent and impatient longing for missing food or absent nurser and any ungranted wish."[28]

Miron (1961) reported on a cross linguistic investigation of phonetic symbolism. Using consonants and vowels found in both English and Japanese language forms, he asked a group of seventy-nine totally English speaking raters and a group of forty-one Japanese and English speaking raters to rate vowels and consonants in terms of pleasant or weak and unpleasant or strong. He reported, "the mean judgments for all subjects in both groups indicated a general trend toward evaluating the front vowels and consonants as 'pleasant' and 'weak' and the back vowels and consonants as more 'unpleasant' and 'strong'."[29]

Perhaps the greatest contributor to a study of phonetic symbolism as suggested by Sapir (1926) was Werner (1932, 1957, 1963). In 1932, he spoke of sounds having physiognomic qualities. In a later book, he further described the concept of physiognomic qualities as follows:

"It has been repeatedly emphasized that on the primitive level the objective world is experienced for the most part in terms of its dynamic properties. Things-of-action reveal expressive, physiognomic qualities. A wooden object 'behaves' differently from a stone object. We look at these objects in a different way, we handle them in a characteristically different way. And yet we do not have to handle them physically in order to experience their dynamic qualities. We can see the heaviness, clumsiness, and durability of stone things, and the lightness, pliability, and splintery qualities of wood. In other words behavioral, expressive physiognomic qualities are not limited to a certain field; they are not specifically kinesthetic, optical, tactual, etc., in nature. In fact, they are intersensory qualities.

"We may therefore speak in a very real sense not only of the softness of velvet, but also of the softness of a color or a voice.

---

[28]Jakobson (52), p. 30.
[29]Miron (71), p. 69.

Expressive physiognomic qualities that are intersensory in character may exist in the sounds articulated by the human voice. That is, language itself has a physiognomic character."[30]

Werner in his last sentences talks about both speech and language as we have defined it. In a subsequent book published with Kaplan (1963), he makes continued reference to the phonetic symbolism not only of sounds but also of language. Finally, Brown (1958) summarized many of the previously mentioned studies and presented some of the modern psycholinguistic conceptualizations of language and sound. Another useful reference to round out our consideration of sound is the volume edited by Saporta (1961), a book of interest chiefly because of the presentation of linguists' views of sounds. Unfortunately, no additional light was shed on the possibility of psychical meanings attached to sound.

Other Considerations

Before turning to our hypotheses, we need to consider some elements of phonetic theory and some aspects of the organic basis for sound production. One of the most extensive systems for understanding phonetic parameters was proposed by Shoup (1963). This work, unfortunately beyond the scope of the present paper for review purposes, illustrates the complexity of sound. Furthermore, it emphasizes that the present formulations are of necessity in a primitive stage. Utilization of Shoup's complex system for the classification of sounds and the systematic relation of the elements of this classification to psychological dimensions appears to be a fruitful avenue for further study.

Shoup considered the primary parameters in her classification of sounds to be *the place where a sound is articulated* (for example, the lips are together in producing the sound *p*) and *the manner of articulation* (for example, there is constriction of the air path generating turbulence at the point of constriction as in the sound *f*). Shoup's secondary parameters in classifying phonemes were *air direction, laryngeal action, air path* and *lip shape*. Further parameters which she discussed as optional in classifying phonemes were *place modification, cavity modification* and *plosive modification*. Finally,

---

[30]Werner (135), pp. 256-257.

she also described sounds as advanced, retracted, elevated, depressed, dentalized and frictionalized.

Utilizing Shoup's classification one might describe many variations (allophones) in the usual listings of sounds. The following chart from Carrell and Tiffany (1960) indicates the usually recognized sounds of American speech.

PHONEMES OF AMERICAN SPEECH

(Reproduced from Carrell and Tiffany: *Phonetics: Theory and Application to Speech Improvement.* New York, McGraw-Hill, 1960.)

Vowels

Front Vowels			Back Vowels		
Symbol*	Key**		Symbol	Key	
[i]	heed	[hid]	[u]	who'd	[hud]
[ɪ]	hid	[hɪd]	[ʊ]	hood	[hʊd]
[e]	hayed	[hed]	[o]	hoed	[hod]
[ɛ]	head	[hɛd]	[ɔ]	hawed	[hɔd]
[æ]	had	[hæd]	[ɑ]	hod	[hɑd]
Central Vowels			Diphthongs†		
[ɝ-ɜ]***	hurt	[hɝt]	[aɪ]	file	[faɪl]
[ʌ]	hut	[hʌt]	[aʊ]	fowl	[faʊl]
[ɚ-ə]	under	[ʌndɚ]	[ɔɪ]	foil	[fɔɪl]
[ə]	about	[əbaʊt]	[ju]	fuel	[fjul]

Consonants

Stops			Fricatives		
[p]	pen	[pɛn]	[f]	few	[fju]
[b]	Ben	[bɛn]	[v]	view	[vju]
[t]	ten	[tɛn]	[θ]	thigh	[θaɪ]
[d]	den	[dɛn]	[ð]	thy	[ðaɪ]
[k]	Kay	[ke]	[h]	hay	[he]
[g]	gay	[ge]	[s]	say	[se]
[tʃ]	chew	[tʃu]	[ʃ]	shay	[ʃe]
[dʒ]	Jew	[dʒu]	[z]	bays	[bez]
			[ʒ]	beige	[beʒ]
Nasals and Lateral			Glides		
[m]	some	[sʌm]	[w]	way	[we]
[n]	sun	[sʌn]	[hw]	whey	[hwe]
[ŋ]	sung	[sʌŋ]	[j]	yea	[je]
[l]	lay	[le]	[r]	ray	[re]

*International Phonetic Alphabet Symbols. (This footnote and the one following designated by** were added to the original text by the present authors.)

**International Phonetic Alphabet Symbols are used for transcription of the key word.

***[ɝ] and [ə] are the "r-colored" vowels. [ɜ] and [ə] are the pronunciations typical of r vowels in Eastern, Southern, and English Speech.

†Does not include the "nondistinctive" and centering diphthongs.

A discussion of some of the acoustic dynamics affecting articulation of sounds was presented in texts by Carrell and Tiffany (1960) and by Thomas (1947). According to Carrell and Tiffany, the changes that occur in individual sounds when they are put together in meaningful connected communication are explained by:

> "(1) The role of *movement* in determining the nature of speech sounds; (2) the *influence* of consonants on vowels; (3) *assimilation,* or the interaction of adjacent sounds on one another; (4) *blending and juncture* or the movement from word to word and syllable to syllable; and (5) *stress* or the effect of the intensity or force of utterance on the nature of speech sounds."[31]

Furthermore, Carrell and Tiffany felt that these parameters, when combined with the psychological characteristics of sound (that is pitch, quality, loudness and duration) help explain what happens to sounds in connected speech.

Both Thomas and Carrell and Tiffany discussed the various regional types of American pronunciation and their peculiar phonetic characteristics. For example, there are three general pronunciation patterns, General American, Southern and Eastern. Although these classifications suggest the region where each pattern of articulation is used, variance exists in each region. A complete exposition of the variance, as well as other facets of phonetic theory, such as normal production of speech, is outside the scope of the present work. The aforementioned texts provide excellent reference works for the interested reader.

Organic Causes of Sound Deviation

Before presenting our specific formulation of ways in which personality organization is reflected in speech, we must also discuss the organic causes which may lay behind deviations in sound. These were discussed in a comprehensive outline by Moore (1957) under the headings of pitch, loudness, quality, and resonance.

Moore suggested that a high pitch may be a clinical result of (1) lack of growth of the larynx to the normal size; (2) some organic problems such as a laryngeal web; and (3) an abnormal approximation of the vocal cords. He noted several organic reasons

---

[31]Carrell and Tiffany (17), pp. 242-243.

for abnormally low pitch, stating: "Three possible pathological causes of low pitch have been observed in the clinic with which the writer is associated: hormonal therapy, growths, and nerve damage."[32] Deafness was the only organic reason Moore offered for abnormal loudness in an individual's voice.

Under quality defects, Moore discussed the problems of aphonia, breathy voice, hoarseness, and harshness. He listed as organic reasons for aphonia: (1) adductor paralysis; (2) ankylosis of the cricoarytenoid joint or joints; (3) the presence of an interarytenoid mass large enough to prevent approximation; (4) surgical removal of one or both cords; (5) the presence of a growth on, or adjacent to, the cords in such a position as to prohibit their vibration; and (6) excessive stiffness from scar tissue, thickened tissue, or edema preventing oscillation of the cords in the air stream.

Organic reasons for breathy voice included an involvement of one as opposed to both vocal cords, and restricted areas of pathology or small growths. Moore differentiated hoarseness into the categories of dry hoarseness, wet hoarseness, and rough hoarseness. He felt that the physiological conditions determining dry hoarseness were similar to those determining a breathy voice. He felt the condition of wet hoarseness occurred "when something in the larynx creates noises which are heard as part of, and in addition to, vocal cord sounds."[33] This condition might be caused by such organic factors as (1) excessive, sticky mucus on the vocal cords; (2) relative flabbiness of one or both of the vocal cords; (3) additions to the mass of cords; (4) the destruction of all or part of a cord. Rough hoarseness was considered to be caused by essentially the same factors as wet hoarseness.

Moore lists two main voice anomalies of resonance—nasality and denasality—as resulting from organic factors. Detection of nasality is usually not difficult. Similarly when the passage of air through the normal opening of the nose is blocked, an individual is likely to suffer from a lack of adequate nasality, or in other words to be *denasal*. It should be recognized that some workers do not feel denasality can be properly labeled a voice problem. For example,

---

[32]Moore (72), p. 659.
[33]Moore (72), p. 664.

Curtis (1956) and Fairbanks (1960) view the problem as a difficulty with articulation. In this paper we have taken the position that denasality represents a resonance (voice) problem.

There are obviously a substantial number of organic bases for deviations of the voiced sounds in human language. In any discussion of organic factors which may influence voice, there must be a discussion of the normal physical changes which occur around the time of puberty. The fact that these are related to voice change must be considered when judgments are made relative to the psychological significance of the voice.

Weiss (1950) made a comprehensive review of the important organic factors in distortions of voice, emphasizing the role of the endocrine gland, the anterior-posterior growth of the male larynx during adolescence, the increase in height of the female larynx during adolescence, changes in the mucosa of the larynx, the atrophy of the tonsil and adenoids, and most importantly, "the growth of the body, especially its bony and cartilaginous structure."[34] For a more detailed discussion, the reader is referred to articles by Moore (1957), Weiss (1950), and to the works of Jackson and Jackson (1942), and Ballenger and Ballenger (1957).

With this background, we are now ready to present several working assumptions relating to the psychological significance of the use of sounds of human speech. We hope these assumptions will be communicable ideas which may begin to bridge the gaps noted in the reported research. Following this presentation, we shall show how these ideas were tested by applying them to a group of children who had been studied and observed for more than a decade.

---

[34]Weiss (133), p. 133.

Chapter III

The Formulation of Working Assumptions in the Present Study

Our Theoretical Orientation

The ORTHODOX ways of considering (the sounds of) speech have been reviewed. In this section of the paper, we propose a new way of understanding some aspects of human behavior through an examination of the use of the sounds of speech. Broadly stated, sounds of speech are conceived as one of the means by which an individual establishes and subsequently enlarges his relationships with society. As such, these sounds are important in reflecting his basic drives and competencies, that is, his successes and failures in relationships with his fellow man. Furthermore, since these sounds may be categorized as either vowels or consonants, and as either voiced or unvoiced sounds, the form of their articulation expresses identifiable drives and defensive maneuvers. Specifically, the vowels are conceived as capable of transmitting man's sexual and aggressive drives. As these drives become modified with increasing maturation, so the vowels may become modified. Consonants are considered to transmit the nature and quality of defensive behavior which the individual utilizes in establishing relationships. As such, consonants are susceptible to modification by developmental factors, and in some instances may become indicators of pathological personality development or functioning. Thus far, we have focused on the broad meaning these sounds may have when used to communicate. It is also our contention that these elements may be imbued by the hearer with a meaning which is analogous to their expressive use.

After the formulation of these general concepts, while reviewing related literature, we discovered an article by Greenson (1954). Although one can never be sure of one's own originality, it came nevertheless as a surprise to find Greenson's formulation regarding the general functioning of the utterance of sounds to be analogous

[25]

in many respects to that which we have just expressed. Hoping to clarify any confusing statements we have made and also to acknowledge that his formulation of the basic concepts studied in this research obviously antedated ours, we present part of his formulation verbatim:

> "(1) The utterance of a sound is a discharge expressive of pleasure or pain, it accompanies instinctual activities and is an indicator of affects. (2) The utterance of sounds has an autoerotic component. Any of the organs of articulation may be the site of some autoerotic component. Other sounds of a more explosive nature offer the possibility of satisfying the aggressive instincts. The auditory perception of sounds and the feeling of mastery that may accompany the production of sounds can also serve as a source of pleasure. The tension discharge function and the autoerotic function of producing sounds can be readily observed in the babbling of infants, particularly of deaf children. (3) The utterance of sounds is a means of interpersonal communication in the form of language. This is the last function of speech to be developed and is dependent upon the successful development of object relations as well as the maintenance of the proper admixture of autoerotic and expressive functions of speech."[35]

In a later paper Greenson (1961) expanded on specific instances where sounds may have symbolic meanings. He wrote:

> "Great emotions are wordless but not soundless. Panic, rage, grief and ecstasy are not expressed in speech but in sound. So, too, is the orgasm. An involuntary cry, gasp, moan, or laugh usually accompanies these intense emotional states.
>
> "The sound can become the auditory representation of the mood —an affect equivalent. For example, the sound "Mm . . ." when produced with a humming or musical intonation indicates a pleasurable oral or gastronomic experience. This linkage between the sound "Mm . . ." and the contented oral experience apparently transcends the boundaries of language. The word for mother in many different languages begins with the sound "Mm . . .". This may be derived from the universal experience of the infant nursing at the breast. The sound "Mm . . ." is the

---

[35]Greenson (37), p. 237.

only sound (the author really means consonant), that one can make with the lips continually closed, i.e., with a nipple safely in the mouth.

"Perhaps a careful study of other moods may reveal that they too are linked to specific sounds. It is noteworthy that in the development of speech in the infant, the first sounds uttered by the infant are uttered in pain and are vowels. Only later does the infant produce sounds in comfort and they are consonants."[36]

The foregoing remarks by Greenson appear to provide support for the assumptions we have earlier stated.

At the beginning of this paper we noted that Freud (1901) alluded to the possibility of the potential psychical meanings implied not only by words but also by sounds. In his *Psychopathology of Every Day Life* he wrote:

"Among the slips of the tongue that I have collected myself, I can find hardly one in which I should be obliged to trace the disturbance of speech simply and solely to what Wundt (1900) calls the 'contact effect of sounds.' I almost invariably discover a disturbing influence in addition which comes from something *outside* the intended utterance; and the disturbing element is either a single thought that has remained unconscious, which manifests itself in the slip of the tongue and which can often be brought to consciousness only by means of searching analysis, or it is a more general psychical motive force which is directed against the entire utterance."[37]

Freud was not ready to commit himself to say that all slips of the tongue centering on sounds were caused by the aforementioned dynamics. Rather he felt that there are some situations where slips of the tongue may be a factor of the phonetic laws. His moderation seems to have been based on his understanding of the work of Meringer and Mayer (1895). Meringer and Mayer classed slips of tongue into such categories as transpositions, anticipations, perseverations and contaminations. Many of these classifications were earlier statements of the laws of assimilation juncture, stress, etc., as noted in our discussion of the books on phonetics by Thomas (1947) and

---

[36]Greenson (38), pp. 80-81 (Comment in parenthesis is ours.)
[37]Freud (31), p. 61.

Carrell and Tiffany (1960). However, it should be noted that Freud believed Meringer to have attributed to sounds a psychical valency. The authors of this paper would agree with both Meringer and Freud. Our purpose in the present pages is to share our first approximation of the parameters affecting the psychical valency sounds may have.

Hartmann (1939) also addressed himself in a broad way to the concept we are proposing when he spoke about the development of language and other ego-functions. He wrote:

> ". . . I am certainly not implying that these and other pertinent childhood activities remain untouched by psychic conflicts, nor do I imply that disturbances in their development do not give rise to conflicts, or are not woven into other conflicts. On the contrary, I want to emphasize that their vicissitudes play a great role in the well-known typical and individual instinctual developments and conflicts in that they may facilitate or inhibit the individual's ability to master such conflicts."[38]

Finally, Brody (1956) appears to agree with our formulation in writing:

> "Thus also it appears that the development of infant speech proceeds in a continuous dovetailing relationship with other aspects of development that are inseparable from the vicissitudes of instinctual satisfaction."[39]

Having stated our theoretical orientation in a general form, we next turn to a more specific and detailed presentation of our assumptions. While we feel strongly that our major hypotheses concerning the dynamic implications of the use of sound are valid, we realize that some modifications or refinements may be needed. We hope that others who may wish to investigate the validity of our hypotheses will modify or change them where needed.

The Clinical Significance of Distorted Vowels

As stated above, we assumed that vowels as used in oral communication serve the primary function of the auditory expression of sexual

[38]Hartmann (40), pp. 365-366.
[39]Brody (12), p. 369

and aggressive drives. To appreciate the significance of vowels as a means for man's early expression of his drives, it is necessary to consider the raw data concerning the sound elements available early in life. Irwin's (1946) summary of relative vowel and consonant frequencies during the first thirty months of life demonstrates our conception of the verbal expression of drive. For example, mean scores for infants computed on a two-month basis showed that during the first two months approximately 80 percent of the infant's vocalizations are vowels. There is a steady decline in the vowel-consonant ratio until thirty months of age when approximately 50 percent are consonants.

But what is the nature of the sound which is expressed in vowels in early life? Moses (1954) stated that by about the second or third month of life, rage is indicated by screaming, and love by the child's soft sounds which compose his cooing and gurgling. The sounds which make up these expressions are mainly vowels. It is of more than passing interest that man's basic instincts seem to manifest themselves so early in life.

The significance and predominance of vowels early in infancy has been recognized by other writers such as Stern (1928), Lewis (1930), and Greenson (1961). One cue as to how these vowels may be related to the expression of the various drives was given by Lewis in his observation:

> "When the child is in a state of comfort he tends to utter vowels
> of less determinate character than when he is uncomfortable."[40]

The basic nature of vowels is also exemplified by the observation of their early stabilization in the sounds of speech as compared to what happens to consonants. That is, little fluctuation in the ability to make isolated vowels occurs after age three, whereas few children consistantly articulate all consonants in their correct form by this age. These facts were noted in a normative study by Templin (1957), who found fourteen of seventeen vowels and diphthongs were said correctly at age three by at least 90 percent of the children studied. In contrast, only eighteen of sixty single consonant elements were said correctly at age three by 90 percent of the children studied. At age three, 90 percent of the children

---

[40]Lewis (59), p. 25.

studied said none of the seventy-one double consonant blends correctly. Finally, at age three, 90 percent of the children studied said none of nineteen triple consonant blends correctly.

Not only does a child use sounds early in his life but he also responds to auditory sensations. Schachtel (1959) highlighted this aspect for us when he wrote:

> "While Freud thought at first no sensory quality is perceived but that only pleasure or unpleasure are felt in the interior of the psychic apparatus, actually the exteroceptors function from the first day of life (and most of them already in utero) and convey sensory quality as well as give rise to comfort and discomfort feelings."[41]

While discussing tactile, thermal, pressure, and proprioceptive sensations he noted:

> "Together with olfactory and to a lesser extent autocentric auditory sensations they are more important at first in the infants 'recognition' of the nursing situation and of the mothering one than are visual factors."[42]

Niederland (1958) also believed in the child's early ability to have auditory experiences. He wrote:

> "It is well to remember that the influence of auditory experiences, present from the infant's first cry, never stops throughout life, whereas visual contact with the outer world is established only sometime later in infancy, can be relinquished at will, and hardly exists in relation to the 'inner' largely invisible world."[43]

Lewis (1930) summarized the infant's ability to respond to sound in a differential manner. He wrote:

> "Apart perhaps from his first month, the child's responses to speech are never exclusively due either to the intrinsic affective character of what he hears or to training by the conditions in which it occurs. Both factors are present in the child's second month and continue to be present for the rest of his life."[44]

---

[41]Schachtel (109), p. 117.
[42]Schachtel (109), p. 138.
[43]Niederland (85), p. 488.
[44]Lewis (59), p. 47.

Qualifying Remarks

We wish now to specify some of our hypotheses or working assumptions concerning the relationship between vowels and consonants and personality. Parenthetically, we should state our position that the hypotheses which follow are to be considered as working statements to which later research may give more precise formulation. We are aware of the danger of equating any single symptom with any specific psychic phenomenon. However, for expository purposes, presenting the material in this manner seems easier and hopefully clearer to a reader. Furthermore, as a later section of this paper which deals with results will indicate, the significance attached to a specific speech symptom is modified considerably by the interaction of other factors which are combined in ways peculiar to each individual subject. It is this latter position which we, of course, feel must be taken in any clinical use of the concepts we present.

Working Assumptions Concerning Vowel Distortions

We have noted that sound occurs in both vowels and consonants. The five following working assumptions are concerned primarily with the misuse of vowel sounds when no organic basis is present.

Working assumption 1: Persistent hoarseness in the sounds of speech (vowels) tends to occur in individuals manifesting socially distorted sexual identification and functioning.

It will be recalled we postulated that vowels allow the verbal expression of both sexual and aggressive drives. When the phenomenon of hoarseness is present without organic deviations, it is our contention that this hoarseness is related to some deviant aspect of the sexual drive.

Since the term hoarseness is sometimes confusing, we need to define our meaning. By hoarseness we mean a raspy, rough-sounding voice which may vary from mild hoarseness detectable only by an experienced listener to severe hoarseness easily identified by a casual listener.

Our assumption is that hoarseness of any degree results from an attempt to phonate at a level below the individual's optimal or expectable pitch. It will be immediately recognized that the crucial point in this discussion is the motivation for phonating at such a low level. In the absence of organic pathology, the female subjects who phonate at too low a pitch seem to be striving to imitate or identify with masculine models. This assertion brings up two concepts which in many ways are hard to define: that is, the concepts of masculinity and femininity. These are not poles of a simple dichotomy; neither aspect is totally present or absent in any one person. The issue is most clearly stated by Freud (1900) in his discussion of bisexuality, a concept which has been recognized more recently in writings by various psychological and anthropological writers, including Terman and Tyler (1954), Watson (1959), and Mead (1949). Part of the difficulty in using these concepts is that many readers tend to react in an all or none fashion to a statement suggesting that they might have some feminine as well as masculine components in their personality. However, the concept of bisexuality as used by the above writers does not imply the value judgment of good or bad. The question of degrees of femininity and masculinity in an individual becomes important only when the two components are out of balance for a given person living in a specific culture. Watson (1959) made this point when he stated, "But personality differences between men and women in a given culture are largely dictated by the goals of socialization in that culture."[45] Rabban (1950) demonstrated experimentally the impact social groups have on sex-role identification.

In our culture, men and women are assigned or expected to have certain roles and patterns of behavior including certain characteristics of voice quality and pitch. In the course of normal development, we customarily expect boys to want to be like their fathers and girls to be like their mothers. Furthermore, sex-role stereotypes equate passivity with femininity and aggressivity with masculinity. The persistence of a dichotomy in the expected role for the two sexes is generally confirmed by numerous writers (Goodenough, 1931, Watson, 1959, and Sears *et. al.*, 1957). Keeping in mind the problems inherent in postulating that an individual child is striving to achieve a role characteristic of the opposite sex, we

---

[45]Watson (131), p. 441.

have found it worthwhile to relate the use of sounds by individuals to the cultural stereotypes expected of them. Thus, we feel that the person who consistently uses the sound normally attributed to the opposite sex is displaying a type of pathological vocal behavior. For example, the girl who speaks in a hoarse voice without organic pathology is giving a signal of a drive which for her is culturally out of balance. A girl may have a hoarse voice because she wants to sound like a man, or because she has identified closely with her mother who sustains a hoarse voice. If the mother's hoarse voice is organically determined and all other aspects of the girl's personality are developing normally, then one would expect the girl's hoarseness to be transitory since she could be expected to drop this manner of phonating because of its basic inefficiency and inappropriateness in her culture. However, when hoarseness in the mother represents masculine strivings, and when the girl has made a satisfactory identification with her mother, then she might be expected to continue being hoarse. An interview with the mother in this instance would clarify substantially the meaning we could ascribe to hoarseness. Hoarseness is, of course, only one symptom. In our final judgments of the psychological significance of sounds, we combine a variety of sound behavior before making our judgment. The way in which components of sound behavior are combined will be illustrated in detail in our analysis of the data from the present experiment.

The meaning of hoarseness in males presents some new issues. While the etiology, i.e., attempting to phonate at too low a pitch, is the same, the motivation is different. Our present assumption is that a boy phonates at too low a pitch as a result of external and/or internal demands for assertion of his masculinity. For example, these demands may be made by an emotionally-ill mother who sees in her boy a substitute for an inadequate or absent husband. The boy's concept of masculinity, developed primarily through perception of the father, may be a factor. And finally, hoarseness in males may result from premature attempts at expressions of sexuality. This leads us to believe that transitory hoarseness in males is not always pathognomic. We refer specifically to the normal male's competition with the father for the mother. While hoarseness is postulated as typically occurring in a boy at the height of his oedipal struggle, it still has importance as a signal of the possible meaning of the moment to the boy. To illustrate the value of considering hoarseness in a clinical context, we present the following case example, which illustrates what we consider to be hoarseness of a pathological degree. It is a case example from clinical practice and is not taken from the subjects of the present research sample.

> The patient, a fourteen-year-old boy, was referred because of increasing behavior disorders. The most pronounced feature about his communication abilities was a definitely hoarse voice. This difficulty had persisted since age five according to the parents. There were no periods in which he lost his voice entirely and he received no special help for this condition. To study some of the possible dynamics of the problem, he was asked to put on a puppet show with a mother, father, boy and girl puppet. When talking as a father doll, his voice continued to show hoarseness. In talking as the boy doll, his voice dramatically improved and no hoarseness was present. During the observation he also played a game of war with toy soldiers which were present. As the mock battle grew more severe, there was also a noticeable lessening of hoarseness, suggesting that the hoarseness could also be connected with the feelings he was discharging during his play. With regard to the continued hoarseness exhibited while playing the part of the father, the psychological examination supported the thesis that he was in the midst of continuing oedipal struggles which had never been resolved.

We have already presented a discussion of organic factors which affect voice quality. It should be re-emphasized that organic factors must always be ruled out prior to speculation such as we have advanced. In our opinion there are certain types of sound disturbances which, though apparently organically caused, may be related to the individual's personality. We refer specifically to the phenomenon of vocal nodules. These are growths appearing on the cords and interfering with the smooth contact of the cords against themselves and in the subsequent pure production of sound. The resultant sound produced often has a hoarse quality. Nodules are customarily considered by laryngologists to be a result of vocal misuse (cf Ballenger and Ballenger, 1957, Jackson and Jackson, 1946). But this explanation does not attempt to determine why the child originally misused his voice. We have previously stated our hypothesis as to why a child misuses his voice and becomes hoarse. To us it would also seem possible that the continued misuse of voice necessary to produce hoarseness might be an expression of masochistic tendencies on the part of the child. We have not attempted to discuss hoarseness from the standpoint of different types, i.e., wet, dry, etc. Moore's (1957) breakdown into these different categories might give added depth to our formulation.

Working assumption 2: Deviation from culturally accepted pitch levels is associated with a distorted sense of sexual identity.

Our earlier discussion of organic causes of deviation in culturally accepted pitch must be kept constantly in mind as we discuss this hypothesis. We must also keep in mind the pitch stereotypes which are culturally expected of men and women. There are wide variations of tolerance in the pitch one may use, but in this discussion we will refer to both the subtle and extreme variations which the experienced diagnostician can detect. In a gross sense, society has come to expect a man to have a voice pitched lower than a woman. If we equate the pitch of the voice a person uses with Freud's (1905) concept of the sexual object, we have a basis for speculating as to the psychological significance of the deviant pitch. In individuals who without organic reasons persist in using a pitch not culturally accepted, it would appear possible that pitch may have reached the level of a fetish. Freud's discussion of the significance of the fetish, in part, is as follows:

> "The situation only becomes pathological when the longing for the fetish passes beyond the point of being merely a necessary condition attached to the sexual object and actually takes the place of a normal aim, and, further, when the fetish becomes detached from a particular individual and becomes the *sole* sexual object."[46]

Translation of this possibility on the clinical level where a sound disorder occurs suggests that the continuance of a pitch higher

---

[46]Freud (33), p. 146.

than usual, in a boy where organic factors are excluded, reflects among other things a primary feminine identification process. When the boy is unconcerned about the high pitch, we speculate that a more serious problem is present. Although there are probably exceptions, we still wish to advance the thought that the tendency toward homosexuality must be greater in males who have no concern over their high-pitched voice. Moses (1954), in essence, also suggested this formulation. On the other hand when a boy with a high-pitched voice expresses discomfort in regard to his voice, we envisage him as in conflict over the process which is occurring.

In girls, the permanent adoption of a pitch lower than usual* in the absence of organic causative factors suggests the emergence of a masculine sexual drive. This process may be encouraged by pathological familial interactions. Some girls voluntarily state that they adopt a low-pitched voice because it sounds "sexy." Their admission adds some weight to our feeling that pitch is related to the sexual drive. While some girls adopt a low pitch in an effort to be sexy, the low pitch of others may result as a side effect of their strivings toward an aggressive masculine role in life. There are undoubtedly elements of sexuality in the attempt to adopt this role, but they seem to be qualitatively different. In addition, it is possible that a girl who openly admits she has adopted a low voice in order to sound sexy has a stronger drive towards overt as opposed to latent homosexuality. She is, in other words, attempting to be sexy not primarily for the purpose of attracting a male, but to be sexy by adopting a male-sounding voice to seduce other women. In the low pitch of the female who is openly striving toward a masculine role in life, seduction is not always a major factor. Rather, we postulate that the primary goal is the discharge of aggressions in a typical male fashion.

In this discussion of possible psychological implications of pitch, a brief side excursion is appropriate. It is commonly believed that the pubertal change of voice produces a dramatic episode in the

---

*The impact a given cultural setting may have on adoption of a lower pitch is important to note. However, the opinion of the authors is that since speaking at too low a pitch is uneconomical in terms of physical effort, that continuance of this habit can only occur where masculinity finds a suitable outlet in the expressive modality of pitch. The current vogue of low-pitched female night club singers is thought to be a manifestation of the above assumption.

life of most children. Especially in boys, it is commonly supposed that a sudden creaking and groaning occurs in the attempt to phonate. In practice this notion seems to be more romantic than real. Weiss (1950) proposes this same idea when he states: "Most frequently the normal mutational change of the voice proceeds gradually . . ."[47] The usual reason offered for a child's sudden loss of control is that the sudden physiological spurt of growth temporarily makes him physiologically unable to control the functioning of his cords. To the present writers' knowledge, there has been no substantiation of the belief that rapid physiological growth in boys causes loss of control of pitch. Rather than explaining loss of pitch control by reference to the growth spurt, we postulate the operation of psychological factors. With the approach of adolescence, various age-typical psychological stresses are normally resolved and the appropriate sex role assigned by society is adopted. As a part of this normal process, appropriate pitch is established. At this point in time, therefore, change or lack of change in voice seems to be more, or at least equally related to psychological growth than to the associated physiological growth.

Working assumption 3: Restriction of range of the voice occurs in individuals whose normal expression of the sexual drive is constricted by emotional factors.

Ordinarily, every individual manifests some range in the pitch of his voice. The reduced range of some individuals may be explained either on a physiological or a psychological basis. Sometimes both are operative. Observations of children referred for psychiatric evaluations suggest that restricted range of pitch, when also accompanied by hoarseness, tends to occur in individuals with disturbed thought processes. Moses (1954) commented extensively on restriction of pitch range in psychiatric patients of various diagnostic classifications. The interested reader is referred to his text for more detail.

Working assumption 4: Deviations in the sounds of voice described as breathy tend to occur where sexuality is repressed or denied.

A breathy sound, as noted earlier, may result from organic factors

---

[47]Weiss (133), p. 149.

or from other sources. In a broad sense, breathiness, or the sub-stitution of whispering for phonation, can be thought of as a type of dysphonia or aphonia, depending on the extent of the breathiness. In contrast to the aphonia or dysphonia in which lack of phonation is assumed to be an unconscious phenomenon, breathiness, at least at its onset, is in many persons a conscious act. Motivation for the act is, however, probably unconscious. This phenomenon in our experience tends to occur primarily in teen-age girls. During this time, the girl is vocally identifying with someone other than her own mother. Since we hypothesize that full use of sound is one expression of normal discharge of the sexual drive, breathiness then seems to indicate the contrary. In other words, breathiness reflects suppression or repression of sexual drive. It is a paradox that a breathy voice is considered by some as a sexy voice, for if our hypothesis is correct, it is almost the opposite in a symbolic sense in the mind of its user.

Working assumption 5: The sounds of harshness and nasality express aggression.

We have already postulated that the voice as expressed in vowels transmits derivatives of the sexual drive. The present hypothesis postulates that the aggressive drive may also be expressed in vowels. Society tolerates wide ranges of nasality and harshness, as was also true of pitch. Likewise, we should again emphasize the possible organic causes. The topic of harshness has been discussed in terms of its organic etiology previously. Nasality is thought to occur as a consequence of a lack or an insufficient amount of palatopharyngeal closure. Nasality is often heard in individuals with a cleft palate or some congenital insufficiency of the soft palate. Barring the presence of such organic deviations, we feel that the use of a nasal or harsh sound is a verbal expression of the aggressive drive. Whereas the individual with a harsh voice is thought to be mani-festing this drive more overtly, the person sustaining only nasality is thought of as a predominantly passive-aggressive personality. Varying degrees of nasality may be present. The cultural norms and accept-ance of degrees of nasality obviously are important variables which influence our judgment. In some individuals, with or without nasality, there is a sort of a whine. This added dimension in our scheme is equated with the immature, demanding, and childish aspects of the person. Our basic assumption is that a whine is an expression of aggression at a neurotic level whereas nasality in the absence of organic factors is considered to be a characterological expression of aggression.

The Clinical Significance of Misarticulated Consonants

In the broad statement of our formulation, it was postulated that articulation of consonant sounds is a type of defensive behavior utilized by a person in the process of establishing relationships. As such, consonants reflect satisfactory or unsatisfactory developmental experiences. Correct usage of consonant sounds is extremely important since it is by this means that one's sounds and language become intelligible to others. Whereas vowels provide the carrying power for speech, consonants transmit intelligibility. We believe that vowels transmit information about how certain drives are handled and that consonants show aspects of how relationships are formed with others.

Part of the meaning of consonants as indicators of relationships can be deduced from past research. Thus, reports by Freud and Burlingham (1944), Spitz (1957), Rheingold (1956), and more recently Provence and Lipton (1962), all emphasize the relative unintelligibility of institutionalized children's speech and language in comparison with the normal child's speech and language development. It will be remembered that we assume intelligibility is a function of consonants. Therefore, we should expect that the main difficulty in the intelligibility of sound in the institutionalized children would be with consonants. Freud and Burlingham (1944) emphasized the function of consonants, as we have described them in this paper, in their observation that some children develop a special form of communication with their mothers differing from that used daily with the personnel who cared for them. Freud and Burlingham's observation emphasizes the significance of sounds as reflectors of relationships with others. Following our hypothesis, it would seem that these institutionalized children developed special defenses (manifested by unintelligible speech) in the environment in which they lived and relinquished them when they were with their mothers.

Irwin (1947 and 1948) demonstrated that by twelve months,

the child has said correctly, in his free vocalization, all the consonants and vowels which will be used in later adult speech. Why should it be, then, that it takes a child so much longer to use correctly consonants in words than the vowels? Customarily this phenomenon has been explained as an example of maturation and learning. We prefer to interpret the data as suggesting that incorrectly produced consonants commonly thought to be normal developmental errors, serve pregenital defensive functions which the individual relinquishes only after he has worked himself through the patterns of this period of his life.

On the following pages, we shall present our observations and speculations regarding the meanings of certain specific deviations or inaccuracies in the use of consonants. To date, we have been unable to observe a pattern for all the consonant sounds found in the English language as spoken in the United States. Indeed our findings may be even more limited since all the children observed were from one Midwestern metropolitan area.

Certain consonant sounds have appeared most productive for our study. These are the *s* as in *c*ity or *s*it; *r* as in *r*an; the *r* [ɜ·]* as in bu*rr;* the *l* as in *l*ady; the *f* as in *f*ather; *d* as in *d*og; the *th* [θ] as in *th*ank; and the *th* [ð] as in *th*em. These sounds are often interchanged with each other when misarticulated; hence, they must be discussed from a larger context of observed behavior rather than solely from the context of the individual sound.

Working Assumptions Concerning Consonant Misarticulation

Working assumption 6: Persistence of the frontal lisp (substitution of the *th* [θ] sound as in *th*ank, for *s* as in *s*it or *c*ity) occurs in individuals who maintain a pregenital level of personality development.

This idea has been expressed in varying ways by other writers (Moses 1954, Van Riper 1954). Although these writers did not state the hypothesis in exactly the same form, they addressed themselves to the question as follows. Moses (1954) felt that continued lisping at an adult level was an expression of continued need for

---

*Bracketed symbols are International Phonetic Alphabet Symbols.

infantile oral gratification. One of us stated in an earlier publication (Rousey and Toussieng, 1963) that lisping seems to occur in individuals who maintain a prolonged and infantile manner of relating to society. In our experience continued lisping in adults tends to occur more frequently in women than in men. In its early stages, society often rewards lisping by praising it as "cute." Thus, we speculated that individuals who maintain this deviant sound behavior are usually infantile, passive, feminine, and dependent in their relationships with others. While this form of relating may be modified by other factors, the substitution of voiceless *th* for *s* without the presence of other factors or other extenuating circumstances ostensibly occurs in people with this type of personality.

Working assumption 7: Lateral lisping (a spilling of air over the sides of the tongue in articulating the *s*) appears in individuals whose narcissism has reached a pathological degree.

Lisping has variations. The form we discussed earlier was called a frontal lisp. Sometimes the air is spilled over the side of the tongue and a slurping sound is produced. This we refer to as a lateral lisp. The acoustic effect is that of sloppiness and messiness. There also seems to be a diversion from the usual psychological meaning of lisping as presented in our preceding hypothesis. Individuals with this form of sound substitution have in our experience related to society in a sloppy, haphazard way pleasing primarily to themselves. For example, these are the children whose school desks were the messiest. Their personal habits were far below average standards of neatness. Their parents claimed they had the messiest rooms at home. One child we observed (outside the present experimental sample) rubbed candy with evident pleasure on a Rorschach card as he took the test. Although the infantile style of life is present, these individuals have allowed the messy and less particular way of relating to others to become their dominant style of life. They are particularly resistant to change since their tendency is to trust themselves more than others. Lateral lisping seems to be at the severe end of a continuum with frontal lisping seemingly a more hopeful prognostic indicator of possibility for emotional changes.

Working assumption 8: A whistle sound accompanying articulation of the *s* phoneme reflects anxiety in interpersonal relations.

One of the subtle indicators of comfort in any interpersonal communication situation seems to be reflected in the manner in which the *s* phoneme is articulated. This phenomenon was initially noted by one of the authors (Rousey) during his teaching duties in a college community. In that situation, a large number of college students were referred to the college speech clinic with the complaint that they manifested a sharp whistle while articulating the *s* phoneme. It soon became obvious that these referrals were mainly made up of two groups—entering students (especially freshman), and students experiencing difficulties in their college and personal life. Observation of the former group showed that as the new students became comfortable in their new environment, the whistle accompanying the articulation of the *s* phoneme disappeared. Likewise, as the students experiencing difficulties in their college and personal lives resolved the points of concern, their whistles also vanished. Since then, the same phenomenon has been observed in other contexts. For example, when new physicians in a residency program first give oral case reports in front of their supervisors, a marked whistle is often apparent. As they become more confident and relaxed in their new setting, the whistle usually disappears. Beginning public speakers and even many experienced public speakers show this phenomenon in initial phases of their addresses. As they progress and become more in command of their topic and audience, the amount of whistle diminishes.

Bradford and Rousey (1961) demonstrated that a whistle could be induced in a person otherwise capable of articulating a normal *s* sound by creating the stress of failure. From these observations we have concluded that a whistle may be thought of as a somewhat universal reaction to the implied threat of failure or of being unacceptable. Although the symbolism to the person is unclear, in some persons it may occur concomitant with situations the person experiences as psychologically threatening.

Different patterns of emergence of the whistle accompanying the articulation of the *s* sound can be observed. The foregoing illustrations are examples in which the whistle was primarily an indication of signal anxiety. In these cases, transitory difficulty with the whistle reflects adequate coping with anxiety.

Other persons, with a chronic and continuous whistle accompanying their articulation of *s*, seem to manifest a pervasive and basic anxiety which might be expected to interfere in their normal day-to-day functioning. In clinical practice, there is yet another group who are obviously disturbed yet have no whistle accompanying the articulation of the *s*. The significance of this is undoubtedly not simple but our observations suggest that a lack of a whistle accompanying the *s* in situations normally anxiety arousing may be characteristic of individuals whose thought processes are so severely disturbed as to be diagnosed as psychotic.

Working assumption 9: The manner in which the *r* phoneme—(as in rat) and the [ɝ] allophone—(as in burr) are articulated reflects the quality of impulse control.

Of the two sounds noted above, we have come to consider the [ɝ] allophone (as in the word burr when pronounced by a person using General American Speech) to be the most basic indicator of impulse control. Although the [ɝ] is a vowel and the *r* is sometimes called a semi-vowel, we chose to discuss them in the consonant grouping because deviation in their articulation appears to reflect problems in the interaction with society. We believe that individuals who substitute the [3] allophone (as in the word err as it is pronounced by a person using Eastern Speech) for the [ɝ] allophone tend to act impulsively without having any idea about the reasons for their behavior. For example, individuals who make this substitution might be expected to act impulsively, e.g., running away from home or an institution where they have been confined, or striking someone, then expressing apparent sorrow for their acts and for a time demonstrating greater control. However, our experience has shown us that they are likely to continue to experience recurrent difficulties along this line.

With reference to the *r* phoneme (sometimes labeled a semi-vowel instead of a consonant) the important sound substitution is the *w* phoneme. This sound substitution seems in many individuals to herald some basic difficulty in interpersonal relationships. While individuals sustaining trouble with the [ɝ] allophone express their impulses outside as well as within the context of the interpersonal situation in an uncontrollable fashion, those who substitute the *w* for *r* have major difficulty in relationships with other people. They are often described as demanding, irritating and troublesome in social situations. This *w* for *r* sound substitution sometimes is a mild one and only detectable to the experienced listener. In children, where the disguise of impulses is not always as complete as in adults, it is usually easier to detect.

Working assumption 10: Difficulties in father-child relationships are reflected by substitution of the *f* phoneme for the voiceless *th* [θ] phoneme (as in *th*ank) and *v* for the voiced *th* [ð] (as in *th*em).

This substitution seems to occur in families where there has been a disturbed relationship between the father and the child. The sex of the child is not a factor since the substitution occurs with apparently similar meaning in both boys and girls. The child seems to have had a generally poor development of his self-concept and a lack of suitable father-child relationship during his early years. Although the substitution of the *v* for the voiced *th* [ð] as in *th*em is a rather infrequent error, this substitution parallels a history of an intrusive father in terms of the father-child relationship. It should be noted that the *v* sound is the voiced counterpart of the *f* sound. Of course, there may be disturbed parent-child relationships where this substitution does not occur. The conditions surrounding its appearance need to be clarified by futher research.

Working assumption 11: Repression of the expression of anger in interpersonal relationships is associated with substitution of the *d* for voiced *th* [ð] phoneme.

In our clinical experience, this phenomenon has been observed quite often in children after the *f* for voiceless *th* [θ] substitution has been corrected. We speculated that as the child experiences some freedom in expressing aggression towards his father (having resolved this relational aspect), he will for a time continue to substitute the *d* for the *th* [ð] in his interpersonal relationships with others. However, this substitution occurs also where the antecedents are not so clearly defined. For example, this type of sound substitution often is associated with the sound patterns of the so-called "tough guy" from the slums of a large city. Thus, ethnic variables may be important in determining this sound substitution. We would also suggest that in such groups the repressed expression of anger may be equally important.

Working assumption 12: Deprivation of early oral needs is reflected in the manner of articulating the *l* phoneme.

Another sound which seems to have clinical significance is the semi-vowel or consonantal *l* phoneme. In some individuals, this is articulated with a sort of swallowing sound. Some speech pathologists refer to it as a backthroated *l*. Our speculation is that this sound distortion occurs in individuals who have been severely deprived in terms of early satisfactory gratification of their oral needs.

Another variation of disturbance of this sound is the substitution of the *w* for *l* phoneme. The hypothesized basic dynamics are similar with the exception that persons having this substitution often project their need for obtaining gratification and nurturance into interpersonal relationships.

The Clinical Significance of Disturbed Functioning of the Speech Mechanism

Another bit of behavior sampled in a speech evaluation is the functioning of the physical speech mechanism. Although by definition the speech mechanism includes the tongue, lips, teeth, hard and soft palate and the larynx, the structure we found to provide the most psychological cues is the tongue. Our observations about the tongue provide the basis for the next group of hypotheses.

Working assumption 13: The phenomenon of tongue thrust is a reflection of an individual's degree of phallic striving.

The phenomenon of tongue thrusting has only recently received widespread attention by speech pathologists. In essence, the phenomenon is as follows. Instead of retracting the tongue as one swallows, the tongue is protruded. Often the forward pressure against the teeth is thought to produce a severe occlusal problem. The reasons for the development of a tongue thrust are at present largely speculative. One of the most popular beliefs is that the tongue thrust is a result of bottle feeding with a nipple unlike the mother's nipple, resulting in improper swallowing action of the tongue (Straub, 1951). Although there is widespread acceptance of this viewpoint, supporting data seem to be controversial. For example, Moyers (1962) proposed a scheme for differential diagnosis of tongue problems which advances our understanding of the problem to a more complex level. He suggested determining whether the tongue position is a result of (1) abnormal posture; (2) a simple tongue thrust; (3) a complex tongue thrust or, (4) a retained infantile swallow. The resulting malocclusion so often believed to be a function of the tongue thrust may also be, according to Moyers, a function of the other musculature surrounding the teeth, lips, etc. It is of more than passing interest that Moyer's discussion of the retained infantile swallow emphasizes psychological aspects of the person as possible causative agents. The present writers feel that a tongue thrust, or speaking in Moyer's terms, a tongue problem other than that caused by a retained infantile swallow may also be a symptom of psychological problems (cf. Palmer 1962).

The consideration of the tongue thrust as a psychological symptom is not restricted solely to the present research. For example, Kester (1963) viewed the symptom of tongue-thrust swallowing as "a symptom of an underlying mother-child interaction, mediatable by breast or bottle, and would expect the experience to influence the personality of the child, modifiable by other experience, especially an altered mother-child interaction."[48] Observing some children who were tongue thrust swallowers, Kester believes that "Tongue-thrust swallowers tend to show oral fixations. They either expect to receive without effort or belittle that which they receive."[49]

---

[48]Kester (56), p. 284.
[49]Kester (56), p. 285.

It is the position of this paper that tongue thrusting may also be viewed primarily as evidence of phallic striving on the part of the individual. When the commonly held analytic concept of the equation of the tongue with the phallus is utilized, we should expect to find noticeable tongue thrust among persons engaged in masculine striving. Similarly, we might expect to find it among both boys and girls until a proper self-concept is achieved. Many children have a tongue thrust during their earlier years. For example, Fletcher, Casteel and Bradley (1961) noted a high incidence early in life, with rapid decline as the child grew older. Our contention is that these people, who for one reason or another have not relinquished the tongue thrust, tend to persist in this behavior due to a distorted form of phallic striving which has its outlet in this fashion. There is probably an association between a tongue thrust and a lisp since the physical impression of a lisp and a tongue thrust are often the same. In an individual with only a tongue thrust, however, we do not find the kind of immaturity noted in the lisper. It not infrequently happens that individuals with a tongue thrust are acoustically and visually mistaken for the individual who lisps. However, simply turning one's back to a person while he is talking clearly shows that acoustically an individual with a tongue thrust does not necessarily have to lisp. In the present research, we felt that continued tongue thrust was a positive and balancing sign in those boys who also spoke with a high pitch or who showed a tendency toward a passive feminine role. When a tongue thrust was not present in these persons, we felt this was a more serious psychological signal in terms of their personality organization. With respect to the occlusal problem thought to arise as a result of tongue thrusting, we have found that this should also be checked to provide additional evidence of the action of the tongue thrust. However, an occlusal problem may exist as a result of factors other than the tongue thrust. Therefore, to make an over-all prediction of the degree of phallic striving from examination of the speech mechanism, one has to ascertain whether the occlusal problem results from a persisting tongue thrust at present, whether it is from a tongue thrust habit which was discontinued some time ago, or whether the occlusal problem is related to other factors.

Certain Aspects of Neurological Status

Working assumption 14: Diadochokinetic rates for tongue movements are a subtle reflection of the neurological status of an individual.

In the previous working assumptions, we have dealt with the psychological meaning of the various speech sounds and functioning of the speech mechanism. Here we shall describe certain aspects of the neurological status of the individual as they can be measured during a speech evaluation. The procedure used is that of testing the rapidity of contact and relaxation possible for combinations of the various points of sound articulation. For example, phonation with rapid closing and opening of the lips results in the sound *b*. The number of times this can be done in a ten-second period is the individual's diadochokinetic rate. A minimal diadochokinetic rate (Westlake, 1951) for elevating the tip of the tongue to a point behind the upper teeth is presumed to be ten times in ten seconds. This is slower than that of the average person but nevertheless sufficient for producing the sounds utilized in language in an intelligible fashion. Some individuals have a smooth and rapid pattern of diadochokinesis. Others have hesitant and broken patterns. Some people start off well but eventually bog down. This bogging down can be compared to the difficulty one experiences as he enters an increasingly sticky substance in which he was at first able to run quite easily. It is our speculation that such qualitative differences, even when they occur along with the quantitative sufficiency needed for intelligible speech, reflect minor neurological impairment. This impairment, usually described as an indication of "soft neurological signs," is sometimes picked up in psychological tests. Testing diadochokinesis in a group of twenty-one subjects (other than those previously studied), Rousey and Toussieng (1963) were able to predict correctly the presence or absence of soft neurological signs in fifteen subjects, when other tests conducted by the neurologist and other psychiatric team members were used as criterion measures. Where disagreements occurred, a certain stable pattern was present. Thus, in five of the six children where normal diadochokinetic rates were reported, the only positive neurological finding was an abnormal EEG. In the remaining case, the child had von Recklinghausen's disease. Some as yet unpublished material by Fletcher (1964) dealing with normative data for diadochokinesis will give the diognostician other evidence to work with in detecting signs of neurological malfunctioning in the speech mechanism.

Clinical Implications of Sound Rejection

Up to this point, we have talked about the expressive or motor aspects of communication. We shall now consider the receptive aspects of sound, an area usually explored by audiologists and otologists by standard audiometric and otologic procedures. A detailed discussion of the techniques of an audiological evaluation would lead us too far from the purposes of this presentation. The actual details are part of a body of knowledge of the large field of audiology and could only inappropriately and incompletely be summarized at this juncture. Interested readers are referred to books by Hirsch (1952), Newby (1958), and Jerger (1963). However, one aspect of the reception of sound which has not been explored extensively by the audiological group is the significance of rejection of the various sounds of speech which we shall discuss briefly in relation to our working assumption 15.

Working assumption 15: The sounds which are heard may have symbolic meanings similar to those postulated for sounds which are used and misused in verbal communication.

In the present study, this hypothesis has been explored by the administration of the Wepman Test of Auditory Discrimination (1958). In the Wepman Test, the individual is asked to indicate whether two words said consecutively are the same or different. Our observations during testing of children show some rather consistent errors. For example, children who have been unable to achieve a satisfactory relationship with their father, and who manifest this problem in their own speech by a sound substitution of f for the voiceless *th* [θ], often have difficulty in differentiating sameness and difference between heard words where the only discriminating item is the f and the voiceless *th* [θ] sound. This phenomenon might be used by some speech pathologists as evidence that there is an auditory perceptual problem at the root of the speech difficulty. Such an explanation fails to take account of the fact that such a receptive difficulty may occur where no expressive difficulty exists in speech. The auditory perceptual explanation also fails to consider the fact that there must be a perceiver in any auditory perceptual process. The presence of a perceiver immediately introduces complex personality factors into any equation of perception. The basic difficulties most frequently occurring in auditory perception as measured by the Wepman Test, as we have used it, have been substitution of the *f* for voiceless *th* [θ], and *v* for voiced *th* [θ]. It is hypothesized that these difficulties have their explanations in a rejection of the phoneme which they symbolize in an expressive sense. These implications have been discussed earlier in this paper. No consistent pattern of difficulty has been noted with other sounds. However, in the same way that we have not completely understood all of the symbolic meanings of sounds used in an expressive sense, we should also state that we do not understand all the symbolic meanings which may become attached to sounds used from a receptive standpoint.

Other Clinical Inferences Possible From Speech and Hearing Evaluations

Other psychological dimensions can be predicted from a study of how sounds are heard and used. For example, there seems to be a basis for predicting relative functioning of verbal and performance skills on intellectual tests. Our working assumption and the rationale accompanying it are as follows:

Working assumption 16: The presence of a speech defect or admitted fear or dislike for verbal participation usually suggests a higher score on performance tests than on verbal tests as measured by standard tests of intelligence.

It has already been fairly well-established that individuals with sound difficulties have lower verbal than performance I.Q. scores. Diedrich (1958), and Rousey and Averill (1963) have pointed this out, to name only a few. However, this relationship is sometimes influenced by other factors. For example, children with mild sound difficulties or fear of speaking in groups sometimes over-compensate in the verbal sphere, thus obviating the rule inherent in our hypothesis. In such a case, either essentially similar I.Q. or a higher verbal I.Q. would be expected.

Working assumption 17: The presence of a speech difficulty at the time of an evaluation is presumptive of earlier speech problems.

Although this hypothesis is believed to be invariant, there are aspects which are not always clear. For example, there is no way to postdict the severity of past sound difficulties from the present behavior. There is also no way to postdict the existence of sound difficulties in the past if they are not currently manifested.

The following section presents the results of the application of the foregoing working assumptions to the speech behavior exhibited by twenty-four normal children comprising part of the group being studied by L. B. Murphy and her colleagues at The Menninger Foundation. How much clinical insights on the part of the examining speech pathologist influenced the judgments cannot be stated. However, an attempt was made to form the judgment primarily on the basis of the working assumptions we have made and to describe the children in terms of the implications of these hypotheses as we have stated them.

Chapter IV

Method of Study

Procedures in the Speech and Hearing Evaluation of Twenty-four Prepuberty Children

WITHOUT KNOWLEDGE of previous psychological, psychiatric, or physical examinations or observations, or of social or developmental history, except as reported by the child, one of us* examined the speech and hearing of twenty-four prepuberty-aged children from an intensively studied normal sample. In doing this the following series of standard procedures were employed: (1) A brief interview of each child in regard to his experiences and feelings about speech development, capacity for and interest in verbal communication; (2) measurement of auditory sensitivity by response to pure tones at the frequencies of 250 cps, 500 cps, 1000 cps, 2000 cps, 4000 cps, and 8000 cps; (3) measurement of auditory discrimination of common speech sounds as they occur in initial, medial, or final positions in words as given in the Wepman Auditory Discrimination Test; (4) examination of the peripheral speech mechanism, that is, the structural aspects of the oral apparatus, and study of the diadochokinetic rates, i.e., capacity for use of the speech mechanism as indicated by quantitative and qualitative aspects of the rate and accuracy of sound production in repetitive articulation of the phonemes [bʌ], [dʌ], [lʌ], and [gʌ]; and (5) oral reading of sentences from the Templin-Darley Tests of Articulation (1960) allowing the clinical evaluation of pitch, intensity, voice quality, and accuracy of producing speech sounds in a meaningful context.

It is important to remember that these evaluations were based primarily on certain relatively objective normative expectations of the range of speech behavior appropriate for the age and sex of the subjects, but more subjective clinical impressions from the quality of the interpersonal interchange during the examination could not

*All clinical examinations and inferences were made by Dr. Rousey.

be entirely excluded. The speech evaluation was made in a situation which, while it was intended to be permissive, was yet inherently mildly tension-arousing insofar as it required the child to respond verbally to a male adult examiner and to carry on tasks which though not generally highly emotionally charged were in some instances unusual or strange in the child's experiences. Thus while postdictions were predominantly made on the basis of objective findings or cues from the child's speech, interpersonal factors were always present and may in some instances have influenced the postdictions.

Assessment of Postdictions

Assessment of the postdictions was complicated to some extent by the fact that the number of postdictions necessarily varied from child to child as dictated by the number of speech deviations or idiosyncrasies which actually appeared in the individual evaluations. For example, thirteen postdictions were made on one child (Vivian) in contrast to seven postdictions on another child (Chester). These differences in the number of postdictions resulted from the fact that Chester showed no gross articulatory errors, in contrast to Vivian, who made several substitutions.

Table A shows the total number of postdictions made for each individual child and for the group as a whole. For example, thirteen postdictions were made on one child; twelve postdictions were made on one child, eleven postdictions were made on four children, and so on. In all, 233 postdictions were made for the sample as a whole.

For each individual child, we have recorded specific postdictions, along with the speech signs, and other clinical observations or history contributing to the specific postdictions. Each individual postdiction was then assessed by the co-author of this manuscript* for level of accuracy as reflected by congruence with other data which was at the time of the postdiction unknown to her colleague. Individual psychiatric evaluations made at prepuberty by Dr. Povl Toussieng, Psychiatrist, The Menninger Foundation, were major sources of validation data. However we also relied upon reports of

---

*All assessments and ratings were made solely by Dr. Moriarty.

structured and projective tests, academic records, social history, conference notes, physical examinations, and other observational records. Attempting to integrate all these sources of validation, each postdiction was rated on a 0 to 5 scale of accuracy, interpreted as follows:

5—accurate and fully documented

4—predominately accurate, but with mild discrepancy in the data or modulation in the degree of weight assigned to the variable

3—partially accurate; partially inaccurate

2—predominatly inaccurate, but with mild discrepancy or modulation in the degree of weight assigned to the variable

1—inaccurate; data conflict

0—no evidence, inappropriate or not verified

These numerical assessments with accompanying comments as to the source of the validation data were often extremely thought-provoking and meaningful clinically, but they posed a number of problems statistically since we had no way of determining expectable distribution on such a rating scale. Following a conference with a statistician,** the authors decided to collapse the assessment scale into a three-way division of postdictions which were accurate or predominantly accurate, those which were inaccurate or predominantly inaccurate, and those which for any reason were felt to be inappropriate or unsubstantiated by the known data. This procedure permitted us to assess level of accuracy of the postdictions from four points of view:

First, we were able to assess level of accuracy for individual children in terms of the number of correct postdictions in relation to the total number of postdictions made for the individual child; that is, we measured the degree of accuracy for individual children in terms of the percent of postdictions which were correct. Second, we were able to look at the total number of postdictions made and to compute the percent of accuracy for the group as a whole.

Third, we tried to group the total number of postdictions in terms of several broad classifications of the area in which the postdictions were made. Our assumption here was that it might be

---

**Miss Lolafaye Coyne of the Research Staff at the Menninger Foundation.

TABLE A

CHILDREN GROUPED BY NUMBER OF POSTDICTIONS

Number of Postdictions per Child	Number of Children	Names of Children	Age at Time of Speech Evaluation	Total Postdictions For Each Group
13	1	Vivian	11-9	13
12	1	Susan	13-10	12
11	4	Terry	14-4	44
		Ray	11-9	
		Rachel	12-11	
		Martin	14-0	
10	8	Roddy	13-5	80
		Teddy	14-2	
		Greg	14-0	
		Diane	12-3	
		Vernon	13-4	
		Lenny	11-7	
		Donald	12-1	
		Karen	13-6	
9	5	Sheila	11-6	45
		Steve	13-11	
		Darlene	12-1	
		Sally	11-10	
		Janice	14-2	
8	4	Gordon	13-10	32
		Daryl	13-1	
		Barby	13-5	
		Ronald	12-8	
7	1	Chester	13-7	7

Total Postdictions for 24 Children: 233

easier or more feasible to postdict certain kinds of behavioral data. These areas included:

(1) the presence and form of manifestation of anxiety or tension;

(2) the onset of speech, pace of speech development and vulnerability in the speech area;

(3) the child's capacity for and way of relating to the father;

(4) the child's capacity for and way of relating to the mother;

(5) family relationships considered more generally;

(6) self-concept and identity;

(7) the direction of identification and quality or descriptive aspects of the process of identification;

(8) neurological factors;

(9) the balance between verbal and performance functioning as reflected by scores on the Wechsler Intelligence Scale for Children;

(10) aspects of personality structure or adjustment.

Fourth, we hoped to assess the validity of the specific working assumptions as they were stated and discussed in Chapter III. That is, aside from the validation of the major hypothesis, that speech reflects dynamic relationships in the developmental process, we sought to check the assumptions that specific speech cues could be associated with specific aspects of behavior.

We felt that the projective use of a routine speech evaluation, as we have outlined it, is an exciting clinical advance warranting further exploration. Thus we present the findings which follow with full awareness that our statistical analysis was primitive and therefore should be regarded as suggestive rather than definitive. Furthermore, a more elaborate statistical analysis did not seem to be feasible because the size of our pilot sample was small and because there were technical problems in establishing the validity of the ratings themselves. The internal consistency of the ratings and the conclusions drawn from them suggested a kind of face validity. We were aware that a more rigorous test of validity demands application of these techniques to a larger sample whose speech patterns and the related postdictions might then be assessed by two independent raters. At the present time, several practical considerations made this more scientific methodological handling of the data impossible. For example, the co-author of this report was the only staff member with previous training in speech problems and thus fully conversant with the theoretical assumptions or hypotheses on which the postdictions were made. Nor did other staff members have the time required to acquaint themselves with the conceptual scheme or to review the accumulated quantity of potentially validating data. We felt that the potential usefulness of such a systematic study of the uses of speech dictated formulation and assessment of the underlying assumptions for immediate publication rather than waiting until the system had been perfected. It was with these limitations in mind that our current summary statement about the accuracy of the speech postdictions was made.

Chapter V

Results of the Study

Accuracy of the Postdictions on Individual Children

Looking first at the level of accuracy of the postdictions for individual children, we found a rather broad range of level of accuracy varying from 50 percent to 100 percent. For one child, Lenny, only 50 percent or five of the ten postdictions made were assessed as accurate. On the other hand, for three children, Teddy, Ray and Sally, all of the postdictions made were considered accurate. That is, ten postdictions made on Teddy were judged to be validated by other data; eleven postdictions made on Ray, and nine postdictions on Sally were considered correct by the rater. Complete records illustrating the process of judging the validity of the postdictions are given for Ray, Vivian, Lenny and Chester in Chapter VI.

Problems in Assessing Postdictions

Parenthetically, we might speculate on reasons for such differences in level of postdictive accuracy. Although there may be other factors involved, two sources of potential error occurred to us. First, aside from the apparent validity of the association between speech signs and psychological behavior as conceptualized by the senior author, postdictions may in some children have gone astray as a result of a failure to take account of multiple determinants of behavior, or to give sufficient weight to positive balancing factors in the child's total adjustment. For example, in a child like Lenny, his resilience, adaptability, and persistent effort were perhaps not fully activated or observable in an examination by a stranger focusing on the weakest areas of his development. In such a context, resistance to sound intake, correctly assessed to be of significance in the preservation of equilibrium, was seen as an endpoint in functioning, whereas other data suggested rather that it was a contributing aspect, along with other counterbalancing features, specifically social grace, responsiveness, capacity to enjoy, and energy level.

In the same way, Lenny's keen awareness of his sensory difficulties was assumed for theoretical and postdictive purposes to be an index of an unstable self-concept. Although this relationship could easily be documented in other data, it oversimplified the situation by omitting, perhaps because the examination did not elicit it, qualities of vigorous and often quite efficient efforts to compensate for these difficulties. In the sense that Lenny is aware of some deficits in his skills, he is insecure, but his insecurity has not immobilized him; rather it has focused his attention on ways of handling his difficulties, and evoked considerable resourcefulness. From this point of view, the speech evaluation appears to be highly sensitive to resistance and to levels of self-esteem, but it is most useful when combined with other clinical data which may tap different aspects of child behavior.

A second source of error in the postdictions, again not detracting from the probable validity of the conceptual scheme, arose from inconclusive tests or incompleteness in certain areas of the background or validating data. This was most apparent in relation to postdictions about neurological features or early speech development. In the former case, it was not always possible to verify or refute neurological status since we had for economic and practical reasons not routinely given a neurological examination. Since our subjects had not applied for help, we felt that a request for a neurological examination might have seemed unnecessarily threatening to the mothers of some of our subjects. Thus, assessment of accuracy of individual postdictions was in some cases limited to brief or indefinitive comments in the psychiatric or psychological summaries. Furthermore, since postdictions of neurological status were considered only in those cases where positive signs were present in the speech evaluation, assessment of postdictions in the negative direction was of necessity based on the assumption that no mention of neurological factors implied negative findings. While in most cases such an assumption was probably valid, it left room for some doubt, especially when neurological signs were minimal or at least not functionally incapacitating.

Another problem arose in regard to assessment of postdictions about early speech development. Since our data did not include direct observation of the children between approximately six months and three years of age, we were forced to rely on a mother's memory, which we knew from other sources was not always reliable, especially where early speech problems were minimized or forgotten in the face of subsequent improvement. In addition, mothers were not trained to observe, were not familiar with differentiations or terminology and therefore sometimes misrepresented the seriousness or the nature of speech deviations. We knew, for example, of one child who was reported by the mother and the child himself to stutter at an early age, yet both the speech examinations and other data raised serious doubts that this could have been true. In this case, we reasoned that the usual preschool repetitions and halting attempts at expression must have been interpreted by the mother as stuttering, yet technically we felt it was not true stuttering since it was not accompanied by secondary speech characteristics or other behavior usually associated with stuttering. Therefore, it seemed possible that there may have been other faulty interpretations on the part of mothers about speech development, but we have no measure of the frequency with which this occurred.

Summarizing these parenthetical remarks, we felt that inaccuracy in postdictions sometimes arose from known gaps in the data, misinterpretations, or in other cases lack of awareness on the part of the postdictor of other determining factors in expressive style. With these exceptions, level of accuracy was fairly high, tending to support our theoretical assumptions. Our thinking on this matter was supported by the fact that for eighteen children or three-fourths of the sample, postdictions were correct more than three-fourths of the time. For an additional five children, accuracy level ranged from 62 percent to 75 percent.

Findings for the level of accuracy for individual children are given in Table B, which indicates the number of postdictions made, the ratings assigned, and the total level of accuracy. For example, reading across the page we note that nine postdictions were made on the basis of Sheila's speech. Of these, seven were rated 5, that is judged as entirely accurate as reflected by the validating data which is specifically documented in the summary notes on this

Diagnostic Implications of Speech Sounds

child. Furthermore, one additional postdiction was rated 4, or predominantly accurate. One postdiction was felt to be inaccurate. This meant that 89 percent of the postdictions made on the basis of Sheila's speech were felt to be accurate or predominantly accurate as judged on the basis of previous data on this child.

TABLE B

ASSESSMENT OF ACCURACY OF SPEECH
POSTDICTIONS FOR INDIVIDUAL CHILDREN

Name	Number of Postdictions	Ratings						Accuracy			%
		5	4	3	2	1	0	+	−	0	
1. Sheila	9	7	1			1		8	1		89
2. Steve	9	7			2			7	2		78
3. Roddy	10	7	2		1			9	1		90
4. Teddy	10	7	3					10			100
5. Susan	12	9	1	1	1			10	1	1	83
6. Gordon	8	5	2				1	7		1	88
7. Greg	10	7	2			1		9	1		90
8. Terry	11	4	3	1	3			7	3	1	64
9. Darlene	9	4	4	1				8		1	89
10. Diane	10	9				1		9		1	90
11. Chester	7	4	2	1				6		1	86
12. Ray	11	6	5					11			100
13. Sally	9	8	1					9			100
14. Vernon	10	9		1				9		1	90
15. Janice	9	8					1	8		1	89
16. Daryl	8	5	1			2		6	2		75
17. Vivian	13	4	4	3	1	1		8	2	3	62
18. Rachel	11	3	4	4				7		4	64
19. Martin	11	5	3		2	1		8		3	73
20. Lenny	10	3	2	1	4			5	4	1	50
21. Donald	10	6	3	1				9		1	90
22. Karen	10	8	1	1				9		1	90
23. Barby	8	3	4			1		7	1		88
24. Ronald	8	3	4				1	7		1	88

Level of Accuracy for the Sample as a Group

Going on to review the level of accuracy for the total number of postdictions made on all children, we found that 193, or 83 percent of the total number of 233 were accurate or predominantly so. Eighteen postdictions, or eight percent, were rated as inaccurate on the basis of the validating data and twenty-two postdictions, or 9 percent, were judged to be unsubstantiated or indefinitive insofar as they were neither totally accurate nor inaccurate. (That is,

this percentage included all postdictions which were initially rated
3 or 0.)

These findings, though certainly not entirely controlled or scien-
tifically rigorous, were clearly impressive and probably well beyond
chance expectation. They suggested that speech evaluations can
offer much to a practicing clinician whether he be concerned with
speech in the functioning of normal children or with deviant
behavior such as one sees in the typical child guidance clinic. Obviously, the practicing clinician cannot divorce himself from a variety
of subtle cues which he experiences in interacting with the child.
On the other hand, since the present postdictions were based on
specific speech signs, it seemed inevitable to conclude that the form
and quality of speech can do much to focus the attention of an
experienced clinician on some of the major areas of behavior and
adjustment which are of interest to anyone hoping to understand
human behavior.

We can perhaps best illustrate our feelings in regard to the
projective use of speech in a clinical evaluation by examining levels
of the accuracy of postdiction in several major areas. Specifically,
we shall want to explore wherein the postdictions were accurate and
to determine to what degree speech signs were exclusively used in
arriving at them. Furthermore, we shall want to consider whether
certain areas of postdictions are more feasible than others and to
examine sources of error in those postdictions which appeared to
be inaccurate or misleading.

In general, we felt that the postdictions were most successful in
regard to the assessment of identification processes and least successful
in reflecting verbal and performance aspects of cognitive functioning.
In the former case, postdictions regarding the identification process
based on cues from speech might prove to be very useful screening
devices for a large-scale evaluation of mental health status in total
groups or classes of individuals. That speech postdictions were not as
successful in differentiating between levels of cognitive functioning
in verbal and performance areas is probably not surprising nor a
real detriment in the projective use of the speech evaluation.

Level and Quality of Anxiety

Let us now turn to postdictions made in regard to specific areas of behavior. First we shall discuss postdictions made about the level and quality of anxiety or tension as reflected in speech. The postdictions, the speech symptomatology on which they were based, and rating of accuracy are presented in Chart I. In all, twenty-six postdictions were made in regard to anxiety. These postdictions involved twenty-three of the twenty-four children in the sample and all of the postdictions were rated as predominantly correct. In nearly all cases, the postdiction of anxiety was based on the presence of a whistling *s* in the spontaneous speech of the child or on speech elicited in response to specific tests in the speech evaluation. In a number of cases, secondary indices of tension or anxiety such as intensity and quality of the voice or the presence of a lisp contributed to this postdiction. In a relatively few cases, the impression of tension or anxiety was also gained by clinical observations of distorted or unusual motor activity, such as excessive jitteriness, hyperactivity or the presence of tics. In no case, however, was a postdiction made solely on the basis of quality of motor activity. Some comment about anxiety level was made in regard to all children with the exception of Donald. This did not mean that Donald was regarded to be absolutely free of tension or anxiety, but only that tension was not reflected by this particular speech sign. Since twenty-three

CHART I

POSTDICTIONS IN REGARD TO PRESENCE OF ANXIETY

Child	Speech Behavior	Postdictions	Ratings of Success of Postdictions
1. Sheila	Whistle on sibilants, stridency in voice, variability in voice quality, motor restlessness.	Tense, anxious.	5
2. Steve	Sharp whistle on sibilants.	(a) Generalized tension and anxiety with specific castration anxiety.	5
	Minimizes and constricts speech.	(b) Inability to allay anxiety in relation to father.	5
3. Roddy	Variability in intensity of speech. Whistle on sibilants.	Severity of speech problems is handled by compensatory use of speech, keeping him under constant tension and pressure. He is a driven child.	5
4. Teddy	Whistle on sibilant sounds and tic around the eye.	Massive anxiety, related to castration anxiety.	5

CHART I (continued)

POSTDICTIONS IN REGARD TO PRESENCE OF ANXIETY

Child	Speech Behavior	Postdictions	Ratings of Success of Postdictions
5. Susan.	Whistle on sibilant sounds, reticence to speak publicly. Mature, overcontrolled voice combined with a whistle on sibilants.	(a) Vulnerability to stress and castration fears. (b) Conflict about growing up with communication difficulties.	5 5
6. Gordon	Prominent and continous whistle.	Insecure behind facade of indifference.	4
7. Greg	Sharp whistle on sibilant sounds, inability to state whether word pairs were alike or different; for example: vow-thou; wretch-wretch; thread-shred.	Very anxious, self-critical, with castration fears.	5
8. Terry	Whistle on sibilant sounds and efforts to control jitteriness (physical movements).	An anxious child with castration fears.	5
9. Diane	Lisp, whistle on sibilant sounds, meaningless giggle at the end of many speech productions.	She becomes anxious under challenge or stress.	5
10. Chester	Whistle on sibilant sounds.	Anxious in relation to stress.	5
11. Ray	Mild whistle on sibilant sounds, not sustained.	Mild anxiety: controlled and not overwhelming.	5
12. Sally	Consistent whistle on sibilant sounds.	Anxious reaction to challenge or stress.	5
13. Vernon	Prominent whistle on sibilant sounds with extensive perspiring and variability in speech patterns which were worse during the articulation tests.	Anxiety of long standing; but he binds anxiety as long as he can, evades the situation. Under stress anxiety breaks through.	5
14. Janice	No marked whistle on sibilants but some stridency.	Excessive control of affect especially in relation to anxiety.	5
15. Daryl	Mild whistle on sibilants, worse under pressure. Discomfort in talking to adults and particularly in oral work in school.	Anxiety present; adjustment facade vulnerable to pressure.	4
16. Vivian	Very soft voice and a definite whistle on sibilants.	Almost any situation aggravates or elicits tension.	4
17. Rachel	Whistle on sibilants, sound substitutions, lisp.	High level of anxiety, particularly in interpersonal relationships. Little opportunity or capacity for expressing basic personality characteristics.	5

CHART I (continued)

POSTDICTIONS IN REGARD TO PRESENCE OF ANXIETY

Child	Speech Behavior	Postdictions	Ratings of Success of Postdictions
18. Martin	Whistle on sibilants; reported overstimulation to classroom verbal communication. Hill-billy colloquialisms and intonations.	High level of anxiety in the face of challenge or stress. He tries to suppress anxiety and uses speech defensively.	4
19. Karen	She added words to sentences read orally and self-consciously corrected these. No whistle on sibilants.	Anxiety in speech evaluations partly related to adolescent communication problems but also a reflection of anxiety at a deeper level.	5
20. Barby	Whistle on sibilants occasionally and voice quivering but both disappeared rapidly as evaluation progressed.	Mild anxiety in relation to stress but normal in context and she recovered rapidly.	4
21. Ronny	Whistle on sibilants and lateral lisp present during formal tests but not present in casual conversation.	(a) Anxiety present, but not really incapacitating. (b) Some evidence of castration anxiety and some degree of pathological narcissism increasing with stress.	4 5
22. Darlene	Whistle on sibilants increasing with challenge, but she soon becomes aware of this and consciously controls this expression.	Tries hard to control feelings including anxiety, perhaps overly so.	4
23. Lenny	Generally poor speech with intermittent whistle on sibilants, loss of voice and variability in quality of speech.	Speech and communication are highly pressured areas.	5

of the twenty-four children were said to have some level of anxiety, we might assume that the speech evaluation in itself was anxiety-producing. On the basis of our previous work in assessing anxiety in relation to taking structured tests, this is probably not an inaccurate assumption. On the other hand, the examiner was often able to evaluate the degree of anxiety, and sometimes to indicate its source, i.e., appropriate and temporary tension in relation to the evaluation itself or more pervasive and deep-seated anxiety in relation to total adjustment. In those cases where anxiety was specified as related to castration fears it was usually possible to document this in the psychiatric evaluation. In two children, Darlene and Janice, where the speech cue of a whistling *s* was minimal, a postdiction of over-control of feelings, and especially anxiety, was made. In both cases, those postdictions were considered accurate, insofar as overcontrol of feelings was suggested by a variety of other clinical evidence. When Rousey postdicted appropriateness of anxiety level in relation to the situation, he noted capacity for dissipation of anxiety through a variety of coping maneuvers. This insight was particularly cogent in the case of Barby whose anxiety level was in a number of other records considered appropriate and characterized by resilience and recovery.

These findings suggested that the presence of a whistling *s*, particularly if its onset, course and control can be traced in speech patterns, is a valid indication of anxiety. However, we need to be alert to the fact that anxiety of any level may be expressed in a variety of ways and derived from a number of causes which may or may not be apparent in the speech patterns themselves. For example, the reserve and difficulties in verbal communication observed in Vernon expressed a quality of anxiety which is quite different from the anxiety reflected in the hostility and negative aspects of autonomy seen in Daryl. Thus, it seemed to us that anxiety as reflected in the whistling *s* can focus the attention of a competent observer on the presence of anxiety. In so doing, it serves the timesaving function of directing further professional exploration into sources and meaning of surface anxiety.

Onset, Pace of Development and Vulnerability of Speech

The second area of postdictions concerned the onset of speech, the pace of development and vulnerability in the speech area. Specific postdictions for each child together with the rating and speech symptomatology is presented in Chart II. Twenty post-dictions were made on fourteen children. Of these, fourteen were judged to be correct, four as incorrect, and two as not validated or indefinitive. The rate of speech development was judged to be correct in two of the postdictions and incorrect in one. In the one case where the postdiction was judged to be wrong, the fact of the birth of a new baby in the family appeared to modify the course of speech development. Earlier forms of speech distortion were correct in seven cases, wrong in one, and not substantiated in two. Inaccurate postdictions here were possibly accounted for in several cases by faulty memory of the child as reported during the speech evaluation or of the mother as she reported to the project members who obtained the social histories. In one case, the mother may not have been wrong but perhaps misinterpreted normal pre-school hesitations and repetitions as stuttering. One postdiction involving reaction to therapy was judged to be wrong, but here again faulty memory on the part of the mother may have been one aspect of the situation. Vulnerability in the speech area was correctly postdicted in one case and speech background was correctly post-dicted in three cases. In general, we might say that postdiction of earlier speech development was in most cases correct except where mitigating circumstances modified the expected speech development or where faulty memory on the part of the mothers confused the developmental picture. These facts may be clearer by reference to a few specific cases. For example, a slow rate of speech develop-ment was postdicted for Sheila on the basis of the current confusions in her speech. This assumption seemed logical if the pattern of

CHART II

POSTDICTIONS ABOUT SPEECH DEVELOPMENT: ONSET, PACE, VULNERABILITY

Child	Speech Signs	Postdiction	Rating	Comments
1. Sheila:		(a) Slow development of speech with	1	
	Sound substitutions.	(b) marked articulatory errors as young child.	5	
2. Steve:	Inability to recall much about speech therapy; continuation of speech distortions.	Early treatment for stuttering ineffective, or perhaps discontinued too soon.	3	There is conflicting evidence here. The mother said speech problems were "cured," but articulatory errors were prominent in the preschool tests and there were some records of stuttering.
3. Roddy:	Therapy for 1½ years. Current lisp, whistle on sibilants, sound substitutions, loss of voice and secondary stuttering patterns.	Severe early speech problems.	5	

CHART II (continued)

Postdictions About Speech Development: Onset, Pace, Vulnerability

Child	Speech Signs	Postdiction	Rating	Comments
4. Darlene:	Present lisp.	Slow speech development with noticeable distortions in articulation.	4	
5. Ray:	No residue in current speech and no secondary speech mechanisms.	(a) Report of early stuttering seems improbable.	5	
	Teased and threatened in regard to speech.	(b) Considerable tension and pressure accompanying speech.	4	
	Colloquial patterns superimposed on basically good speech.	(c) Quality of speech suggests that Ray comes from a family of low socio-economic status.	5	
6. Sally:	Several regular substitution errors in articulation and difficulties in pronouncing some words.	(a) Variability and consistency of sound substitutions suggests a poor speech environment.	5	Normal onset of speech but articulatory errors were profuse and speech was distinctly vulnerable to stress at several different age levels.
	Frontal and lateral lisp.	(b) Speech development may have been slow. Articulation was probably poor. Communication is well below age level and ability.	4	
7. Vernon:	Laxity and restraint in current speech.	Despite lack of special speech problems, Vernon may have been described by his parents or teachers as having garbled or mushy speech.	5	
8. Daryl:	Lisp.	No reported early speech problems, but she frequently may not have been understood by her parents or perhaps used baby-talk excessively.	1	Unskilled in communication, but mechanics of speech were good. Considerable tension in relating to an adult.
9. Lenny:	Poor present speech.	(a) Marked and persistent speech difficulties in childhood.	5	

CHART II (continued)

POSTDICTIONS ABOUT SPEECH DEVELOPMENT: ONSET, PACE, VULNERABILITY

Child	Speech Signs	Postdiction	Rating	Comments
	Generally poor speech, intermittent whistle on sibilants, loss of voice, variability in speech quality.	(b) Speech and communication are highly pressured areas.	5	
10. Donald:	Lisp.	Probably speech problems were severe at an earlier age with excessive infantilisms and prolonged baby-talk.	5	
11. Karen:	Lateral lisp, *l* sound difficulties.	Probably used baby-talk, which was prolonged because of the rewards she gained.	3	Little baby-talk as such, but a wide range of verbal expressiveness including both very mature and very immature formulations.
12. Ronny:	Continuation of lisp.	Probably had some speech difficulties earlier. His speech may have been distorted or perhaps markedly infantile; jargon remained in his speech longer than most children.	0	
13. Terry:	Continued lisp.	Probably speech problem of long duration.	5	
14. Diane:	Lisp.	Presence of current lisp suggests earlier speech problems.	1	

the family relationships and the child's development remained constant. In Sheila's case, this was probably not true insofar as she appeared to be a much more gratified, self-sufficient individual in infancy than was true of her at a later age when her family, and particularly her mother, were less responsive and accepting of Sheila as a person than had been true in the child's preschool years.

As another example, we may cite the case of Daryl where certain speech distortions were postdicted as occurring in the preschool period. These were not found in the data and hence the postdiction was judged as inaccurate insofar as Daryl's speech was mechanically good and without peculiar articulation. On the other hand, Daryl apparently did experience considerable difficulty in relating to people and in communicating, and in this sense her early speech development was impaired.

Another example is that of Karen in whom excessive baby-talk was postdicted as a preschool child. This postdiction was judged wrong by the rater since baby-talk was not predominant in the speech of Karen although infantilisms were included in the wide range of verbal expression which Karen displayed. In other words, she was capable both of very mature verbal expression at an early age and also of highly immature verbal expression at other times.

One other general conclusion on the basis of these findings is that speech distortion, while highly useful in focusing attention on a specific area of difficulty, should probably never be considered in isolation but rather treated in terms of context and patterns. In the final analysis, while speech evaluations are meaningful for an understanding of the individual child, any single speech cue should lead only to tentative conclusions which can then be flexibly inter-woven with the total pattern of behavior. Just as in the Rorschach interpretation, the presence of a single cue, though potentially symp-tomatic, should be viewed in relation to the total framework of strengths. That is, sometimes strengths more than balance the weak-nesses, which though realistically present, assume lesser significance in the light of the child's total behavior than would appear if the single symptom were considered separately.

Capacity to Relate to Father

Twelve postdictions were made on nine children in regard to the capacity to relate to the father. These postdictions were based mainly on the articulatory substitution of the *f* sound for the voiceless *th* [θ] sound, on deviant pitch or on difficulties in auditory dis-crimination of words different only in the *f* or voiceless *th* [θ], or *v* or voiced *th* [$\eth$]. All of these postdictions were judged essentially correct. The specific statements made on each child and the data on which they are based are shown in Chart III. Although these findings are certainly minimal in terms of number of postdictions, the total accuracy of the postdictions when they appeared strongly suggest that such errors in articulation, deviant pitch or discrimination difficulties with these consonants are associated with conflict in relating to the father. Several auxiliary postdictions in this area were in regard to the dominance of the father or the unavailability of the father. Where these postdictions were made, they were all fully documented in the data. As previously noted, the Wepman Test of Auditory Discrimination was the instrument used to determine the present findings. It should be noted that Byrne (1964) found that the Wepman Test of Auditory Discrimination shows the most errors occurring on *f* and voiceless *th* [θ] and *v* and voiced th [ð] pairs for children within the chronological age range of four and one-half to seven years. Therefore, the present finding, which depends to some extent on the finding of this difficulty, may be criticized as reflecting problems of the test used rather than of the individuals involved. Although this may be correct, the present writers would (1) contend that the present findings are on older children than Byrne used, and (2) speculate that the high incidence of discrimination problems with these sounds noted by Byrne reflects a high incidence of poor father-child relationships present in our society and not a basic weakness of Wepman's test.

CHART III

POSTDICTIONS ABOUT RELATIONSHIP TO FATHER

Child	Speech Signs	Postdiction	Rating
1. Sheila:	Substitution of *f* for *th* [θ] as in *th*ank.	(a) Immaturity; delay or disturbance in resolution of relationship with father.	5
	Difficulties in distinguishing heard sounds, as in the word pair wreath-reef.	(b) Reacts by intolerance.	5
2. Steve:	Difficulties in differentiating between vie and thy, wreath and reef, lave and lathe.	(a) Conflict in perception of father and in efforts to establish relationships.	5
	Passivity in interpersonal relationships, rejection of verbalization, constricted speech.	(b) Attempts to comply with father's demands, but shows much subtle anger against a dominant father.	5
	Difficulties in auditory discrimination, mild hoarseness.	(c) Father too intrusive in demands for son's growth and manliness.	5
3. Roddy:	*v* for *th* [ð] (as in *th*em) substitution, *f* for *th* [θ] (as in *th*ank) substitution, difficulties in auditory discrimination of vow-thou.	Father is not or has not been meaningful figure in Roddy's development.	4

CHART III (continued)

POSTDICTIONS ABOUT RELATIONSHIP TO FATHER

Child	Speech Signs	Postdiction	Rating
4. Teddy:	High pitch and substitution of *f* for *th* [θ] (as in *th*ank).	Lack of suitable father figure in early years.	5
5. Sally:	*f* for *th* [θ] (as in *th*ank) substitution.	Development may have been dictated by lack of a dominant father or by an unusual relationship to her father.	5
6. Vernon:	*f* for *th* [θ] (as in *th*ank) substitution.	Probably had early difficulties in relation with father. Partly sealed over and he has made some adjustment to this problem.	5
7. Vivian:	Whistle on sibilant sounds, *f* for *th* [θ] (as in *th*ank) substitution, low intensity of voice.	Father was either not available or somehow inconsistent as a factor in Vivian's emotional development.	5
8. Martin:	*f* for *th* [θ] (as in *th*ank) substitution.	Basic difficulties in relating to father, perhaps now partly sealed over.	5
9. Karen:	Report of *v - th* [ð] (as in *th*em) earlier substitution.	Relationship to father must have been inadequate or so close that mother tried to modulate it. Symbolically this was an aggressive sound substitution which the mother tried to correct.	4

Relationship to the Mother

Eight postdictions, as shown in Chart IV, were made on seven children in regard to the relationship to their mother. All of these were judged to be correct. In this area, postdictions and the bases on which they were made were so varied that no general conclusions seemed to be warranted.

CHART IV

POSTDICTIONS ABOUT RELATIONSHIP TO MOTHER

Child	Speech Behavior	Postdictions	Rating	Comments
1. Teddy:	Hoarseness and feminine voice quality.	(a) Mother was more available or better able to relate to him.	5	
	Tongue thrust without malocclusion, and poor elevation of tongue tip.	(b) The mother was fairly adequate; she tried to do her best despite the inadequacy of her husband.	4	

CHART IV (continued)

POSTDICTIONS ABOUT RELATIONSHIP TO MOTHER

Child	Speech Behavior	Postdictions	Rating	Comments
2. Gordon:	Tongue thrust and overbite, open spaces in the teeth at the sides.	Intense masculine strivings blunted either by the parents as a unit or by the mother particularly.	5	Marked bitterness toward women.
3. Darlene:	Whistle, tongue thrust.	Conscious hypersuppression of feelings, probably learned from her mother.	5	
4. Ray:	Sound rejection and localized hearing loss; this may have helped him withstand verbal battering from friends and family.	Mother probably described Ray as inattentive, or as behaving as if he were in another world by himself.	4	
5. Janice:	Lack of variability in voice quality.	May have had fairly comfortable early relationship with her mother with subsequent traumatizing experiences.	5	
6. Daryl:	Difficulties in differentiating *v* and *th* sounds. Doubt and lack of confidence in making these discriminations.	Difficulties in the reception of sound with specialized rejection of the mother's voice at the conscious level. She fights off becoming a mother substitute for her younger sibs but does this somewhat passively.	5	
7. Donald:	Tongue thrust and overbite.	The mother may have been a stronger figure in the family and perhaps was unwilling to allow Donald to grow up.	5	

Family Relationships

In regard to family relationships considered more generally, six postdictions were made on five of the children. All of these were judged correct. In most cases, it was postdicted that feelings of rejection or restriction by the parents would be experienced on the part of the child. These postdictions in general were based on intake of sound and suggest that this relationship might well be explored further although the present data does not seem to be extensive enough to warrant general conclusions. Chart V presents the specific statements, accuracy rating, and the data on which the statements were based.

CHART V

POSTDICTIONS ABOUT FAMILY RELATIONSHIPS

Child	Speech Behavior	Postdictions	Rating	Comments
1. Terry:	Long term communication problems with difficulty in the acquisition of consonants.	Probably always experienced difficulties in the degree to which the family accepted him. He always felt not wanted or perhaps family crises made the parents unavailable to him. These feelings must have existed as early as 1 year.	5	Similar speech difficulties in his two younger brothers suggest continuation of family pathology.
2. Diane:	Family feels she cannot talk sometimes. She does not always listen or attend.	Two way interaction of rejection on her part of what is said and of parents' difficulty with or rejection of her for some reason.	5	
3. Chester:	Vacillates in ability to give auditory threshold.	(a) Defensively removes himself from the confusion and noisiness of his large family by not hearing.	4	
	Hoarse, tense voice without a history of neurological problems.	(b) Efforts toward masculine identification complicated by relationship to dominant mother and passive father.	5	
4. Vivian:	Soft voice and motor constraint.	Affective constraint, probably related to inadequate environment with over-restrictions from the parents.	5	
5. Barby:	No distortions in sound discrimination. Occasionally	Normal adolescent rejection of parents on an occasional	5	

CHART V (continued)

POSTDICTIONS ABOUT FAMILY RELATIONSHIPS

Child	Speech Behavior	Postdictions	Rating	Comments
	parents complain she does not understand them.	basis.		
6. Greg:	Difficulties in auditory differentiation of consonants without accompanying hearing loss.	Disruption of family during speech acquisition resulting in inadequate perception of incoming stimuli.	5	

Self-Concept and Identity

Twenty postdictions were made on thirteen children in regard to self-concept and identity. Of these, seventeen were judged as correct, two as wrong, and one as not validated as a result of incorrect weighting. These postdictions were based largely on quality and intensity of voice control or on immaturity of speech development as reflected in a continuing lisp well beyond the age when speech of this sort has normally disappeared. Examples here may help to clarify these findings. In the case of Lenny, the instability of the self-concept as inferred from the speech behavior was to some extent documented by the data, but in the total picture of the child's development, the postdiction appeared to be inaccurate since it failed to take account of the balancing factors of sensitivity and ability to avoid constructively. In the case of Vivian, postdicted difficulties in relating to people as a result of low self-esteem were substantiated in the psychiatric evaluation, but it was modified by the fact that Vivian's problems in this area were not focally involved in her total adjustment. Having adopted attitudes of resignation, she accepted her status with more equanimity than was allowed for in the postdiction itself. The specific postdictions, rating of accuracy, and the data on which they were made are presented in Chart VI.

CHART VI

POSTDICTIONS ABOUT SELF-CONCEPT AND IDENTITY

Child	Speech Behavior	Postdictions	Rating	Comments
1. Sheila:	Blocking and angry helplessness in relation to teasing.	Poorly developed self-concept.	5	

CHART VI (continued)

POSTDICTIONS ABOUT SELF-CONCEPT AND IDENTITY

Child	Speech Behavior	Postdictions	Rating	Comments
2. Teddy:	High pitch and substitution of f for th [θ] (as in *th*ank).	Inadequate development of self-concept.	5	
3. Gordon:	Whistle on sibilants, hoarseness, and his general manner in the evaluation.	(a) Very insecure child who longs for adult contacts and interaction despite a facade of indifference and irritation.	5	
	Whistle on sibilants and trace of a lisp.	(b) Insecurity apparently related to distorted family relationships.	4	
	Facade of indifference, hoarseness, whistle on sibilants and lisp.	(c) He goes through the motions of adopting behavior that looks mature; this serves only as a superficial cover-up for his insecurity.	5	
4. Greg:	Frontal lisp, especially prominent during fatigue.	(a) Active conflict about dependency, infantile self-concept.	5	
	Whistle on sibilants, difficulties with auditory discrimination.	(b) Self-critical and defensive.	5	
	Difficulties in consonant differentiation with absence of faulty vowel differentiation.	(c) Disruption of family during speech acquisition resulted in inaccurate perception of incoming stimuli. Probably followed a period of stability and nurturance.	5	
5. Terry:	Long-time communication difficulties.	(a) He feels not wanted and not accepted by his family.	5	
	Whistle on sibilants and lisp.	(b) Excessive modesty with women.	5	
6. Vernon:	Laxity of articulation.	Unsure of himself; basic lack of security in basic contacts with people, especially parents. He has the usual adolescent problems with some signs of depression.	5	

CHART VI (continued)

POSTDICTIONS ABOUT SELF-CONCEPT AND IDENTITY

Child	Speech Behavior	Postdictions	Rating	Comments
7. Janice:	Inability to differentiate word pair (lave-lathe). She ignores her mother's comments and becomes angry if her peers fail to understand her.	(a) Generalized difficulties in interpersonal relationships; she suffers from feelings of being rejected.	5	
	Lack of inflection in her voice which is usually dull and only rarely pleasant.	(b) Unsure of her own self-worth and basic capacity to handle challenge. She is less resilient than desirable.	5	
8. Daryl:	Speech delivered in whispered form.	Extremely uncertain of herself. No real concept of herself as a person or a woman.	5	
9. Vivian:	Whistle, low intensity of voice, substitution of *f* for *th* [θ], (as in *th*ank).	(a) Difficulties in development of strong self-concept.	5	
	Unusual difficulties in conversing with the examiner.	(b) Extreme difficulties in relating to people.	3	Other records suggest that this postdiction was overstated.
10. Martin:	Difficulties distinguishing vowels.	Early difficulties in developing self-concept as a person and later as a male.	5	
11. Lenny:	Difficulties in phonating and loss of voice control. Much self-doubt but quite comfortable with himself.	Unstable self-concept both earlier and at present.	2	
12. Donald:	Difficulty distinguishing *f* and *th* [θ] (as in *th*anks) sounds.	Poorly developed self-concept because of the lack of a suitable father figure in his development. He may have less difficulty relating to women.	4	
13. Ronny:	Good speech but very hyperactive.	Basically self-assured but hyperactivity serves as an anxiety discharge.	5	

Patterns of Identification

Postdictions regarding the direction of identification were made for each of the twenty-four children and of these, twenty-two were judged to be essentially correct. In two cases, the postdictions were considered incorrect. These findings are summarized in Table C. In most cases, the direction of identification was postdicted on the basis of speech quality as it appeared to be consistent or inconsistent with normative standards of expected voice quality for the sex involved. It is of further interest to note here that in addition to accuracy in postdicting direction of identification, the examiner was generally correct in inferring the presence of conflict, instability, or immaturity in developing patterns of identification. Errors in postdiction in this area appeared to arise only when the speech cue was overassessed without regard to the total framework of the child's behavior.

Beyond assessment of the accuracy of these postdictions, we were impressed with the high level of conflict in establishing identification, as postdicted and validated by other data in the sample as a whole. For example, reference to Table C informs us that only one child of the twenty-four was judged by both speech evaluation and psychiatric interviews to have established appropriate identification with little or no conflict; this was Barby. Five additional girls and six boys were considered to have established appropriate identification but with accompanying conflict, instability or immaturity. Names of the children involved appear in Table C. Two boys were said to have mixed identification patterns, as were two girls. Each

TABLE C

POSTDICTIONS REGARDING DIRECTION OF IDENTIFICATION

	+	−
Appropriate		
Feminine, little conflict (Barby)	1	
Feminine, with conflict, instability or immaturity (Darlene, Diane, Sally, Janice, Karen)	5	
Masculine, with conflict, instability or immaturity (Steve, Gordon, Chester, Ray, Vernon, Ronny)	6	
Mixed		
Boys (Teddy, Terry, Lenny)	2	1
Girls (Susan, Rachel)	2	
Inappropriate with conflict		
Feminine (Roddy, Greg, Martin, Donald)	3	1
Masculine (Sheila, Daryl, Vivian)	3	
	22	2

of these was judged to be correct on the basis of the validating data. One boy, Lenny, was seen as having mixed identification patterns; this postdiction was not validated in the other data. Presumably, although mixed identification was suggested by some of Lenny's behavior, it was more than balanced by other factors in Lenny's development and the error in postdiction arose from faulty weighting of symptomatic cues.

Referring again to Table C, we note that three boys were postdicted to have developed inappropriate patterns of identification with conflict. There were also three girls who were postdicted as having inappropriate masculine identification with associated conflicts. All of these cases appeared to be validated by the data. In one case, that of Martin, the postdiction was made that identification patterns were developing in a feminine direction; this did not appear to be validated in the other data and here again error in postdiction appeared to arise from overevaluation of specific cues without enough regard to the total developmental picture.

Fifteen additional postdictions were made in regard to the identification process. Twelve of these were judged to be correct. These included a variety of descriptive comments about the identification process. They included such disparate remarks as the relative availability of the mother and father, a communality of feelings with the opposite sex, the presence of homosexual trends, the inability to express aggression, the rate of the identification process, difficulty in relating to people, unusual dependency needs, and various comments about defensive maneuvers in the process of identification. For this area, the postdictions, ratings, and the data on which the postdictions are based are found in Chart VII.

CHART VII

POSTDICTIONS ABOUT IDENTIFICATION

Child	Speech Behavior	Postdictions	Rating	Comments
1. Sheila:	Tongue thrust and sound infantilisms.	Identification incomplete; attempts to identify with her father cause confusion and force adoption of some regressive patterns.	5	
2. Steve:	Hoarseness and marked tongue	Despite anxiety and fearfulness in re-	5	

CHART VII (continued)

POSTDICTIONS ABOUT IDENTIFICATION

Child	Speech Behavior	Postdictions	Rating	Comments
	thrust.	lating to father, Steve struggles to achieve male identification. He may have outlets for identification outside the home.		
3. Roddy:	Effeminate speech patterns, hoarseness without organic background.	(a) Superficial identification with his father; primarily identifiies with females and this results in severe problems for him.	5	
	Frontal lisp which is partly controlled.	(b) Infantile traits and pregenital level of development.	5	
4. Teddy:	Hoarseness and tongue thrust along with participation in sports. Hoarseness and lateral lisp with a high pitch.	(a) Currently in ongoing struggle with sexual identification.	5	
		(b) Mother may have been more available or better able to relate to him in his early childhood.	5	
		(c) Feminine qualities in his makeup.	4	
5. Susan:	Overbite and tongue thrust.	(a) Tendency toward masculine identification with prominent phallic strivings. Identification is with her mother but it has some unfeminine qualities.	5	
	Shifts in pattern of relating to experimenter. Evidence of tendencies toward masculine identification.	(b) Perhaps more communality of feelings with males, though this may also be superficial.	2	
6. Gordon:	Hoarseness and whistle on sibilant sounds.	Poor and inadequate identification, but he did not deny or evade these problems.	4	
7. Greg:	Lisp, w for r substitution. Whistle	(a) Tendency toward basically fem-	5	

CHART VII (continued)

POSTDICTIONS ABOUT IDENTIFICATION

Child	Speech Behavior	Postdictions	Rating	Comments
	on sibilant sounds. Feminine voice quality and mannerisms. Rationalization of his lisp with lack of concern about feminine sounding voice.	inine identification, struggle in recognizing masculine development. (b) He might even be ready to adopt homosexual role.	5	
	Mild tongue thrust.	(c) Little overt expression of aggression but strong unexpressed aggressive urges which appear compatible with his feminine orientation.	5	
8. Terry:	Effeminate speech quality with high pitch.	(a) Early strong influence of mother as identification figure around 1 year of age.	4	
	Frontal lisp, discrimination difficulties, high pitch, nasality, lack of tongue thrust suggesting giving up phallic strivings and conflicts about identification.	(b) Difficulties and conflicts in identification; he makes phallic adaptation to feminine identification.	4	
9. Darlene:	A typical tongue thrust.	Massive repression of masculinity has enabled Darlene to make a feminine identification, but it is overly constricted and somewhat distorted. She appears not to enjoy her femininity.	5	
10. Diane:	Frontal lisp.	Undergoing real struggle with family identification.	5	
11. Chester:	Hoarseness and tense voice. Too low pitch with a restricted range.	(a) Active conflict about growing up too soon; he is making unsuccessful efforts to identify with his father too early.	5	
		(b) Phallic strivings not inhibited but developing inappropriately fast.	4	

CHART VII (continued)

POSTDICTIONS ABOUT IDENTIFICATION

Child	Speech Behavior	Postdictions	Rating	Comments
12. Ray:	Unusual hoarseness, too low pitch, mild tongue thrust.	Basic difficulties in sexual identification. Ray overcompensates against pressure from the mother and tries to over-identify with his father.	5	
13. Sally:	Marked tongue thrust and lateral lisp. Voice quality is distinctly feminine.	(a) Probably experiences conflict and struggle in sexual identification. (b) Basically feminine identification despite conflicts.	5 5	
14. Vernon:	Hoarseness, low pitch, emphasis on sports, no tongue thrust.	May be striving for masculinity prematurely. His masculinity is more typical of younger children.	5	
15. Janice:	Variations in appropriateness of voice quality.	Striving for feminine identification, but less advanced than expected for her age.	5	
16. Daryl:	Tongue thrust, overbite, lisp.	Has moved in the direction of masculine identification, but she is infantile.	5	
17. Vivian:	Tongue thrust and overbite. Unusual difficulty in conversing with the examiner.	(a) Preliminary efforts toward identification are in a masculine direction, but parents inhibit this. (b) She has not really reached the level of identification commensurate with her age. She cannot relate to people.	4 3	Probably overstated. She has made some progress in identification with the mother.
18. Rachel:	Overbite, tongue thrust, lisp.	(a) Basic patterns more masculine than feminine, though it appears only indirectly in her behavior. This may be related to her need to stay young and dependent.	3	This was rated 3 because the evidence was not clearcut.

CHART VII (continued)

POSTDICTIONS ABOUT IDENTIFICATION

Child	Speech Behavior	Postdictions	Rating	Comments
	Conflicting signs of masculinity and femininity; hoarseness, tongue thrust, *w* for *r* sound substitution and lisp.	(b) Neither overtly feminine nor covertly masculine reaction patterns have worked out for Rachel; she is not fully identified with either sex.	4	
19. Martin:	Hoarseness; sometimes mistaken for a girl. His tongue thrust suggests efforts to be more masculine.	Basic identification with his mother and he is in conflict about this.	2	Identification is not too stable, but moving in a masculine direction.
20. Lenny:	Difficulties in auditory discrimination; mildly feminine appearance.	Sexual identification primarily feminine or mixed with strong tendencies toward feminine behavior. Efforts to identify with his father present pressure and conflict.	2	He is warmly attached to his mother, but also has strong positive relationships with his father which are well advanced despite his dependency needs.
21. Donald:	No whistle on sibilants suggesting lack of normal fears about developing masculinity.	(a) Has either completely denied his masculinity or completely accepted a feminine role. He may be in conflict about his role.	5	
	Pronounced lateral lisp and high pitch.	(b) More narcissistic than many children. He may be adjusting to his environment in a passive-dependent way with strong tendencies toward feminine behavior.	5	
	High pitch with no hoarseness or whistle on sibilants.	(c) Firm identification with his mother.	5	
	Remarkable contrast between interests and very feminine speech patterns.	(d) Participation in football and his aspirations to be a Marine must be of a defensive nature.	5	
	Clinical inference based on his physical characteristics and above speech behavior.	(e) Obesity may be related to sexual identification problems.	4	
22. Karen:	Continuation of lisp.	Predominantly feminine identification	5	Apparently she was never fully

CHART VII (continued)

POSTDICTIONS ABOUT IDENTIFICATIONS

Child	Speech Behavior	Postdictions	Rating	Comments
		though somewhat immature and in some respects pathological.		compensated for her early oral deprivation but she has handled this by unusual narcissism.
23. Barby:	Pleasant sounding feminine voice quality and pattern.	Normal sexual identification.	4	
24. Ronny:	No tongue thrust or hoarseness. He goes hunting with his father to escape feminine interference.	Good masculine identification but mother probably tries to usurp male prerogatives.	5	

Neurological Background

Twenty-five postdictions were made on twenty-three children in regard to neurological status or background. The specific postdictions and the relevant associated data are noted in Chart VIII. For ten children, positive neurological factors were postdicted. Of these, five were validated by the data; five were neither proved or disproved by previous data, i.e., were inconclusive. In thirteen children, negative neurological findings were postdicted, and of these, ten were validated in the data and three were judged to be inconclusive. In other words, neurological status was postdicted correctly for fifteen of the twenty-three children. For eight children, data was inconclusive. In Chart VIII, we have listed the children on whom these postdictions were made and have indicated the accuracy of the postdictions as judged on the basis of the validating data. For example, a positive neourological background was postdicted in Sheila and this was supported by the data. Negative neurological background was postdicted in the case of Steve and this too was validated by the data. There were no comments as to the neurological status of Greg. On the face of it, these postdictions appear to have held up fairly well, although it was precisely in this area that our validating data were weakest. That is, in most cases we had no formal neurological examination and hence the rater had to rely on casual comments scattered through the records in regard to such factors as structured test patterns, or remarks by the psychiatrist as to deviant speech or motor coordination which could be considered as potential signs of neurological difficulty. Thus, in eight cases the failure to validate postdictions did not necessarily imply that the postdictions were wrong but rather that the evidence was inconclusive or simply omitted in the data.

CHART VIII

POSTDICTIONS ABOUT NEUROLOGICAL BACKGROUND

Child	Speech Behavior	Postdictions	Rating	Comments
1. Sheila	Mild overbite, mild impairment of diadochokinetic rates.	Mild, positive signs of neurological impairment.	4	
2. Steve	Normal diadochokinetic rates.	Negative.	5	
3. Roddy	Qualitative disturbances in diadochokinetic rates.	Mild neurological disturbance, but probably not a major factor in past or present speech difficulty.	5	
4. Teddy	Normal diadochokinetic rates.	Negative neurological findings.	5	
5. Susan	Slow diadochokinetic rates.	Positive neurological findings.	5	
6. Gordon	Normal diadochokinetic rates. Some hearing loss. (Minimal and not really incapacitating.)	Possible neurological background of a low degree.	0	
7. Terry	Wobbly phonation, difficulties in sound integration.	Mild neurological background.	0	Not established though as an infant was considered emotionally labile and it was predicted that he might have seizures.
8. Darlene	Difficulties with *g* phoneme in diadochokinetic tests.	Mild neurological background.	0	Motor awkwardness at preschool.
9. Diane	Normal diadochokinetic rates.	Negative.	5	
10. Chester	Normal diadochokinetic rates.	Negative.	5	
11. Ray	Sound rejection, qualitatively poor diadochokinetic rates and some hearing loss, at 8000 cps.	(a) Minimal neurological signs. (b) Possible lesion of auditory pathway.	4 4	

CHART VIII (continued)

POSTDICTIONS ABOUT NEUROLOGICAL BACKGROUND

Child	*Speech Behavior*	*Postdictions*	*Rating*	*Comments*
12. Sally	Normal diadocho-kinetic rates.	Negative.	0	Never verified, but aphasic-like communication problems at latency.
13. Janice	Qualitatively poor diadochokinetic rates on the *g* phoneme. Jumbled placement of teeth.	Mild neurological signs.	0	Not supported by test patterns and no specific neurological findings.
14. Vernon	Normal speech mechanism and diadochokinteic rates.	Negative neurological findings.	5	
15. Daryl	Normal speech mechanism and diadochokinesis.	Negative neurological findings.	5	
16. Vivian	Normal speech mechanism and diadochokinesis.	Negative neurological findings.	5	
17. Rachel	Normal speech mechanism and diadochokinesis.	Negative neurological findings.	0	Insufficient evidence for differential diagnosis, but Rachel has problems in perspective.
18. Martin	Normal speech mechanism and diadochokinesis.	Negative neurological findings.	5	
19. Lenny	Difficulties with *d* and *g* phonemes, during test of diadochokinesis.	Positive background of neurological difficulty.	5	
20. Donald	Normal diadochokinetic rates.	Negative neurological findings.	0	Disturbances in spatial relationships, fuzzy concrete thinking, prolonged speech problems, all suggest the possibility of a neurological background, although this never was entirely substantiated.
21. Karen	Normal diadochokinetic rates and speech mechanism.	Negative neurological findings.	5	
22. Barby	Normal diadochokinetic rates and speech mechanism.	Negative neurological findings.	5	

CHART VIII (continued)

POSTDICTIONS ABOUT NEUROLOGICAL BACKGROUND

Child	Speech Behavior	Postdictions	Rating	Comments
23. Ronny	Mild qualitative breakdown in diadochokinesis. Some errors in sound discrimination.	Soft neurological signs but not serious enough to interfere with functioning.	0	Concrete and rigid in thinking; no neurological examination.

Verbal-Performance Balance on the Wechsler Intelligence Scale for Children

Twenty-four postdictions were made as to the relative level of skill on the verbal and performance areas of the Wechsler Intelligence Scale for Children. Of these, fifteen or 62.5 percent were correct as validated by the obtained scores on the prepuberty structured test. Seven postdictions or 29 percent were wrong; that is, the child's obtained scores were in the reverse direction from that postdicted. In two cases, the postdictions were judged to be inconclusive since the difference as postdicted, while correct, was so slight as to be essentially meaningless. This was true of Chester where lower verbal scores were postdicted; the obtained Verbal Intelligence Quotient was 118 and the Performance Intelligence Quotient, 120. Furthermore, in the latency test this balance was reversed. In the case of Susan, a lower performance scale was postdicted and while again obtained scores were in this direction, the difference was very slight; the Verbal Intelligence Quotient was 108, and the Performance Intelligence Quotient, 106.

The postdictions made and the assessment of accuracy for each of the twenty-four children are given in Chart IX. For example, we see that a lower Verbal Intelligence Quotient was postdicted for Sheila and that this was found in the obtained data. A lower Performance Intelligence Quotient was postdicted in the case of Teddy and this too was validated by the obtained scores. In only two children were ambiequal balances postdicted. In the case of Janice, this was validated by the data; in the case of Barby this was negated by the data. In all, there were sixteen children for whom lower verbal scores were postdicted. Of these, ten were validated by the data; five were negated by the data, and one appeared to be inconclusive or, in other words, insignificant differences were found. For six children lower performance scores were post-dicted and of these four proved to be correct, one wrong, and one inconclusive.

The postdiction of the verbal-performance balance appeared to be more subject to error than any of the other areas of postdictions. The greater number of postdictions of lower verbal scores perhaps reflected our earlier conviction that performance tests are on the whole easier for children and less conducive to anxiety and dis-comfort. Deviant or distorted speech may be a better indicator of anxiety than a differential reflector of obtained scores. This would suggest that poor speech does not necessarily reflect inability to handle verbal concepts, but rather suggests discomfort or possible vulnerability in this area. Poor speech very possibly is related to difficulties in the capacity to communicate or to relate to others and it is perhaps these areas of functioning which are more congruent with the postdictions than with a measurement of relative skill or basic ability in the two areas of the structured test. It seems possible, too, that these postdictions were thrown off by the fact that the verbal tests in themselves include a variety of subtests, some of which demand social interchange and ability to use verbal concepts in interaction, whereas other tests such as arithmetic involve the use of abstract verbal concepts with little implication for feeling tone. This may have been a factor in the inaccurate postdictions on Daryl, Vivian, and Martin, all of whom excelled in arithmetic, a fact which pulled up their Verbal Intelligence Quotients beyond the level one might have anticipated on the basis of their observed difficulties in relating to people. An additional factor which may have led these postdictions further astray was the presence or absence of certain personality traits such as persistence, obsessiveness, or a proclivity to work slowly. For example, in some children the Perform-ance Intelligence Quotient was lowered beyond the probable level of skill through the slow, careful performance which the child's need for accuracy or perhaps his own lack of confidence dictated.

CHART IX

POSTDICTIONS ABOUT VERBAL-PERFORMANCE BALANCE ON THE WISC

Child	Speech Behavior	Postdictions	Rating	Comments
1. Sheila:	Articulatory errors,	Lower verbal	5	

CHART IX (continued)

POSTDICTIONS ABOUT VERBAL-PERFORMANCE BALANCE ON THE WISC

Child	Speech Behavior	Postdictions	Rating	Comments
	blocking, variability suggesting tension in the speech area.	intelligence.		
2. Steve:	Lack of spontaneity, brevity, inability to communicate optimally.	Lower verbal intelligence.	2	His intelligence test was conducted by a female. Perhaps some change in his capacity to relate to women was more relevant than change in his ability to communicate.
3. Roddy:	Inconsistency of speech problems and verbal aggressiveness.	Lower verbal intelligence.	5	
4. Teddy:	Basically good speech.	Higher verbal intelligence.	5	
5. Susan:	Excellent speech.	Higher verbal intelligence.	3	Potentiality here seems correct though poor physical condition and extreme reticence at the time of the test altered her capacity, or at least the expression and use of it, to some extent.
6. Gordon:	Uncomfortable in communicating with peers or adults, lack of expressiveness in reading.	Lower verbal intelligence.	5	
7. Greg:	Facility with verbal concepts despite atypical speech patterns.	Higher verbal intelligence.	1	
8. Terry:	Complexity, intensity and duration of speech problems.	Higher performance intelligence.	2	
9. Darlene:	Difficulty in talking, she does not enjoy reciting although it is not hard to communicate with her.	Higher verbal intelligence.	5	
10. Diane:	Enthusiastic participation in speech activities.	Higher verbal intelligence.	5	

CHART IX (continued)

POSTDICTIONS ABOUT VERBAL-PERFORMANCE BALANCE ON THE WISC

Child	Speech Behavior	Postdictions	Rating	Comments
11. Chester:	Restriction in range in voice quality and some disturbance in speech patterns.	Higher performance intelligence.	3	True, but the discrepancy is not large and the pattern was reversed in the latency age tests.
12. Ray:	Variety of speech distortions and pressure surrounding speech.	Higher performance intelligence.	5	
13. Sally:	Multiplicity of articulatory and receptive errors.	Higher performance intelligence.	5	
14. Vernon:	Faulty articulation, failure to discriminate sounds, hoarseness and variability in speech patterns.	Higher performance intelligence.	5	
15. Janice:	Minimal speech problems but marked constriction in expressing feelings.	Essentially balanced, verbal-performance functioning.	5	
16. Daryl:	Extreme discomfort in verbal contact, lisp.	Higher performance I.Q.	1	Discomfort does not show up in lowered verbal test scores, though it is obvious in her manner of communicating and relating.
17. Vivian:	Extreme inhibition in use of speech.	Higher performance I.Q.	1	She enjoyed the structured tests and her skills were equivalent in the two areas.
18. Rachel:	Inhibition and poor interpersonal relationships, yet she also apparently likes to use speech in some situations.	Higher performance I.Q.	4	The actual results showed relatively little difference.
19. Martin:	Reticence in classroom recitation, receptive and expressive sound deviations.	Higher performance I.Q. or at least better in academic work which is primarily performance in nature rather than verbal.	1	More at ease in the performance tests but he was best in the arithmetic subtest though total scores in the two parts of the test were very close.
20. Lenny:	Seriousness of present speech difficulties.	Higher performance I.Q.	4	Correct, but difference not great.

CHART IX (continued)

POSTDICTIONS ABOUT VERBAL-PERFORMANCE BALANCE ON THE WISC

Child	Speech Behavior	Postdictions	Rating	Comments
21. Donald:	Seriousness and duration of speech difficulties.	Higher perform- ance I.Q.	4	True, but differ- ence very slight.
22. Karen:	Despite obvious speech problems, Karen handles speech and commu- nications very ade- quately and experi- ences enjoyment in this area.	Verbal I.Q. equals or exceeds perform- ance I.Q.	5	
23. Barby:	Generally good speech.	Higher verbal I.Q.	1	Higher perform- ance I.Q.; more sure of herself on the performance tests. To some ex- tent she seemed to avoid being too vivid.
24. Ronny:	Relatively good speech, enjoyment of speech activi- ties in school.	Higher verbal I.Q.	4	True, but differ- ence not great.

Personality Structure and Adjustment

Fifty-six postdictions were made on twenty-three children on aspects of personality structure and adjustment. These postdictions referred to a variety of comments which could be roughly differ- entiated into three groups, including those items having to do with descriptive comments about character structure, remarks about defense mechanisms and coping maneuvers, and general statements referring to level and quality of adjustment. Considering these post- dictions as a group, 86 percent were judged to be accurate and 14 percent inaccurate or not validated. Where errors occurred, there seemed to be over-estimation of symptomatic behavior without enough attention to favorable balances of positive coping maneuvers. In other words, deviations or distortions in speech were often accurate indicators of poor or faulty adjustment processes, but they sometimes failed to take account of modifying or balancing positive factors which only became obvious in a more complete study of the total pattern of behavior documented in other kinds of data. The variety of postdictions made is illustrated by the data in Chart X.

CHART X

POSTDICTIONS ABOUT ASPECTS OF PERSONALITY STRUCTURE AND ADJUSTMENT

Child	Speech Behavior	Postdictions	Rating	Comments
1. Steve:	Sound rejection, nasality, sullenness.	Passive-aggressive orientation toward the world.	5	
2. Roddy:	(a) Nasality.	(a) Anger in interpersonal relationships.	5	
	(b) Lisp and aggressiveness in interaction.	(b) Narcissism.	5	
	(c) Annual loss of voice in the fall.	(c) Hysterical patterns.	2	Seems overstated.
3. Teddy:	(a) Tongue thrust, hoarseness, and participation in sports.	(a) More comfortable with women and with permissive rather than aggressive males.	4	
	(b) Tenuousness of masculinity as reflected by speech signs noted above.	(b) Difficulties in expressing aggression with males, particularly if they are intrusive or aggressive.	5	
4. Susan:	(a) Excessively neat and orderly. Cold and immobile with the experimenter, superficial warmth later.	(a) Overcontrol and reluctance to show her feelings, especially in interpersonal relationships.	5	
	(b) Lack of variability in voice quality with adult-sounding articulation.	(b) Blunting of sexual drives by emotional factors.	5	
	(c) Excessive control of speech and behavior.	(c) Long time characterological inapproachability.	5	
5. Gordon:	Hoarseness and prominent whistle.	Adjustment very tenuous.	5	
6. Greg:	(a) Occasional *w* for *r* substitution.	(a) Early acting out with aggressive display in school, now partly consolidated.	4	Was this consciously done or unconsciously motivated?
	(b) Markedly feminine voice and mannerisms with rationalization and relative lack of concern.	(b) Needs psychiatric treatment.	5	
	(c) Mild distaste for his reading style.	(c) Some healthy components in adjustment.	5	
	(d) Atypical speech	(d) Probably un-	4	

CHART X (continued)

POSTDICTIONS ABOUT ASPECTS OF PERSONALITY STRUCTURE AND ADJUSTMENT

Child	Speech Behavior	Postdictions	Rating	Comments
	and stress in the classroom situation.	comfortable with male peers and this may emerge in the form of competitiveness.		
7. Terry:	Hearing difficulties reported with no audiometric indication.	Overt physical symptoms reflect difficulties in interpersonal relationships and suggest hysterical components.	4	
	Motor jitteriness and rejection of his auditory environment.	Suppressive devices which impair lack of functioning but do not totally incapacitate him.	5	
	Lateral lisp.	Achieves stability by an unusual degree of narcissism and adopts infantile reaction patterns.	4	
	Discriminatory difficulties.	Considerable unconscious hostility.	5	
	Possible hysterical hearing loss and disturbed diadochokinesis. Long duration of speech problems and feminine identification suggests resistance to therapy if it were to be given.	Therapy is indicated but the family would probably sabatoge it.	3	This actually occurred when Terry was involved in therapy. The current postdiction may be an overstatement of his present problem as he appears to be not too uncomfortable with himself at the present time, although his adjustment may deteriorate when the full pressure of adolescence occurs.
8. Darlene:	Whistle on sibilants increases with challenge but as she becomes aware of it she controls it.	A stable individual but one lacking in vividness and not sufficiently childlike.	4	
	Whistle on sibilants and tongue thrust.	Conscious hypersuppression of feelings learned from her mother.	5	
	Occasional frontal lisp consciously	Occasional spurts of healthy narcis-	4	

CHART X (continued)

POSTDICTIONS ABOUT ASPECTS OF PERSONALITY STRUCTURE AND ADJUSTMENT

Child	Speech Behavior	Postdictions	Rating	Comments
	controlled. She had dull sounding speech and little range or capacity to express joy.	sism. Depressive tendencies with little capacity for gaiety or light-heartedness.	4	
9. Diane:	(a) Inability to differentiate the word "suck" and "sock." Receptive problems in the intake of vowel sounds from early infancy. She fails to use fully her capacity for receiving information. This possibly is related to adolescent development.	She shuts out stimulation from basic features of life and the feelings surrounding them.	5	
	(b) Lateral lisp, protruding incisors suggesting thumb-sucking.	(b) Early oral deprivation.	5	
	(c) Signs as indicated in (b) above.	(c) Intense enjoyment of verbal activity. She may be sublimating early oral deficiencies.	5	
	(d) Signs of early oral deprivation; increasingly poor speech as session proceeded.	(d) Adjustment facade subject to disruption or distortion under pressure.	5	
	(e) See signs given under (b).	(e) Fairly high degree of narcissism, partly handled by displacement in her speech activity.	5	
10. Chester:	Vacillating auditory threshold.	May have a tendency toward hysterical reactions.	4	The labeling of this child as hysterical may be too strong.
11. Ray:	(a) Tolerance of pressure of tension and threats without collapse or development of major speech problems.	(a) Has very strong denial tendency or unusual strength in dealing with speech problems. His effective adaptation to adverse emotional stimulation probably would be reflected in the projective tests.	5	
	(b) Extensive sound rejection.	(b) Defensive reactions against pressures, especially the	4	

CHART X (continued)

Postdictions About Aspects of Personality Structure and Adjustment

Child	Speech Behavior	Postdictions	Rating	Comments
		verbal aggression from the mother.		
12: Sally:	(a) Substitution of *d* for *th* [ð] (as in *them*) and *d* for *t*.	(a) Apparently she is angry at her environment for the role she has been forced to assume.	5	
	(b) She hears tones when none are present.	(b) Hysterical manifestations; perhaps the father was overly involved in her early childhood with current reactions reflecting a repression of these experiences.	5	
13. Vernon:	(a) Laxity and lack of vigor in articulation.	(a) A restrained boy with little zest for living.	5	
	(b) Faulty articulation of *l* sounds.	(b) Early disturbances in nursing and oral development, partly resolved.	5	
	(c) Discriminatory difficulties with the *th* [θ].	(c) Rejects speech of males more than females.	3	Apparently all Vernon's relationships have been relatively distant and there have been no differences noted in the other records.
14. Janice:	(a) Dull voice quality, lack of firmness or stability of tone.	(a) Adjustment to environment is achieved by becoming a distant individual.	5	
	(b) Dull voice with only one breakthrough.	(b) Coping style restricted; capable of much better adjustment than currently mobilized.	5	
15. Daryl:	(a) Whistle on sibilants increasing under stress.	(a) Adjustment facade vulnerable under pressure.	4	
	(b) Lateral and frontal lisp.	(b) Prolonged infantile manner of relating; she is passive, feminine, dependent and highly narcissistic.	5	
16. Vivian:	(a) Extent of constraint in voice and	(a) Reported behavior seems more	4	

CHART X (continued)

POSTDICTIONS ABOUT ASPECTS OF PERSONALITY STRUCTURE AND ADJUSTMENT

Child	*Speech Behavior*	*Postdictions*	*Rating*	*Comments*
	extreme softness of her voice. Reports liking to talk in school and having an interest in speaking out.	a wish than reality.		
	(b) Definite whistle on sibilants and soft whispered speech.	(b) Defense mechanisms appeared to be paper-thin and easily cracked.	4	
	(c) *w* for *r* substitution.	(c) Passive- aggressive tendencies with neutral obstructionist tactics. Probably this is frustrating to adults as is her vagueness and inability to express her feelings and ideas.	5	
	(d) Soft voice and constraint in motor activity.	(d) Constricted emotionally; affective environment lacking in some respects. Her parents probably failed to provide a healthy emotional environment or else overly restricted her.	5	
	(e) Inhibition in verbal expressiveness is extreme.	(e) Anal-retentive behavior problems.	4	
	(f) Extreme inhibition in self-expression.	(f) Highly vulnerable child who needs therapy.	2	Psychiatrist suggests that her resignation in accepting this role decreases her vulnerability.
17. Rachel:	(a) Reported that she would like to be naughty and mischievous. Sound substitutions go along with this.	(a) Basic lack of impulse control, infantile emotional adjustment and early oral deprivation.	4	
	(b) Articulatory substitutions.	(b) Surface adjustment of a mild, gentle, passive, conforming child.	5	
	(c) Difficulty distinguishing several sounds and slight hearing loss.	(c) Tends to reject her environment by shutting out what she doesn't want to hear, but this tendency is modified by	5	

CHART X (continued)

POSTDICTIONS ABOUT ASPECTS OF PERSONALITY STRUCTURE AND ADJUSTMENT

Child	Speech Behavior	Postdictions	Rating	Comments
	(d) Sound rejection without apparent organic basis.	strong conformity drives. (d) Severe adjustment problems arise from a high anxiety level. Her efforts to keep her strong impulses under control increase anxiety. Thus, she has extreme difficulties in relating to others.	4	
	(e) Lowered intensity and pitch and increasing hoarseness.	(e) Under stress, she characteristically withdraws and becomes less feminine.	3	
19. Lenny:	(a) Uneasiness in the session with deviant use of speech and loss of voice. He reported sounds in his ears. There was a prominent whistle on his sibilants though this was intermittent.	(a) Has a deviant and unhealthy resistance to sound intake; psychological basis for denying, shutting out or rejecting what he hears is to protect himself and preserve his equilibrium.	3	This fails to take enough account of his neurological status and the fact that his hearing though not impaired was subject to distortion in his early years.
	(b) Distortions and confusions in discriminating incoming sounds. Hearing sounds not present.	(b) Hysterical components probably appear in the Rorschach.	2	Immaturity, impulsivity, but balanced by control and constructive use of distancing and reality testing.
	Delay in response to discrimination test.	(c) He handles difficulties by staying on guard and may become more schizoid as he gets older.	2	He does use avoidance but on the whole quite constructively.
20. Donald:	Pronounced lateral lisp and high pitch.	Highly narcissistic and may be adjusting to the environment in a passive-dependent mode with strong tendencies toward feminine behavior.	5	
21. Karen:	(a) Generally good speech. She enjoys verbal interactions yet she exhibits a childish giggle and reported difficulties	(a) In many respects completely at ease in the verbal interchange, but there are also signs of immaturity.	5	

CHART X (continued)

Postdictions About Aspects of Personality Structure and Adjustment

Child	Speech Behavior	Postdictions	Rating	Comments
	with *th* [θ|ð] sounds in the past.	Overtly narcissistic.		
	(b) She is very thoughtful in the evaluation and cooperatively accepted the demands of the situation. She reported relinquishing thumb-sucking when she saw that other children did not suck.	(b) She is very much aware of her own feelings and more aware of deeper implications of the evaluation than most children; she appreciated the symbolic aspects of the verbal interchange.	5	
	(c) Frequent lateral lisp and swallowing sound in articulating *l*. Upper incisors protrude, suggesting excessive thumb-sucking.	(c) She must have suffered some form of severe early oral deprivation.	5	
	(d) Lisp and *l* difficulties, along with voluntary relinquishing of thumb-sucking.	(d) Karen tries to control tendencies toward immaturity and her efforts increase the impression of underlying tension.	5	
22. Barby:	(a) Acquisition and development of normal speech with no distortions at present.	(a) A remarkably healthy child in all areas of development including normal sexual identification, resilience and ego strength.	4	
	(b) Slight overbite.	(b) She probably was a thumbsucker as a child, reflecting mild emphasis on orality.	4	
23. Ronny:	Slight overbite.	Gentle, non-aggressive thumb-sucking, erotic in nature but not forceful.	4	

Validity of the Working Assumptions

So far the findings have suggested considerable face validity to our major hypothesis that speech reflects dynamic relationships in human functioning and behavior. Beyond this, what can we say about the validity of the seventeen working assumptions?

Clinical Significance of Distorted Vowels

It will be recalled that we postulated that vowels allow verbal expression of sexual and aggressive drives. Distortions in the vowel sounds are observed in ordinary speech through deviations in voice quality, such as hoarseness, inappropriate pitch, restricted voice range, breathiness and harshness or nasality. In the first five working assumptions each of these speech signs was associated with distortions or inappropriate mobilization of basic drives. In Chart XI, we see that distortions of voice quality, when they were observed, were usually correctly associated with distortions in drives as postdicted. They were, however, so limited in frequency of observation that we must consider the findings of suggestive rather than definitive implication.

Looking at each deviant voice quality, we note that persistent hoarseness was observed in nine children. According to working assumption number one, hoarseness tends to occur in individuals manifesting socially distorted sexual identification and functioning. Assessment of sexual identification by reference to prepuberty psychiatric evaluations showed that eight of the nine postdictions were essentially correct. One child, though he had in the past been unable to make an appropriate sexual identification, seemed well on the way toward more adequate functioning in this area.

We observed six deviations in pitch, that is, pitch which was inappropriate for the sex of the child. In working assumption number two, it was postulated that pitch deviations are associated with a distorted sense of sexual identity. Assessment of clinical data showed that this was substantially true in five of the six cases. In the sixth case, data were controversial and no clinical judgment could be made.

CHART XI

SYMPTOM FREQUENCY AND ACCURACY OF POSTDICTIONS AS RELATED TO
OBSERVED MISUSE OF VOWEL SOUNDS: DISTORTIONS IN VOICE QUALITY

Name	Persistent Hoarseness	Deviations in Pitch	Restricted Voice Range	Breathiness	Harshness or Nasality
Sheila:					
Steve:	+				+ (harsh)
Roddy:	+				+ (nasal)
Teddy:	+	High +			
Susan:					

CHART XI (continued)

SYMPTOM FREQUENCY AND ACCURACY OF POSTDICTIONS AS RELATED TO
OBSERVED MISUSE OF VOWEL SOUNDS: DISTORTIONS IN VOICE QUALITY

Name	Persistent Hoarseness	Deviations in Pitch	Restricted Voice Range	Breathiness	Harshness or Nasality
Gordon:	+				
Greg:		High +			
Terry:		High +			+ (Slight nasality)
Darlene:			+		
Diane:					
Chester:	+		+		
Ray:	+	Too low +			
Sally:					
Vernon:	+				
Janice:			+		+ (nasality)
Daryl:				+	
Vivian:					
Rachel:	+	Low O			
Martin:	—				
Lenny:					
Donald:		High +			
Karen:					
Barby:					
Ronald:					

+ : Correct as validated by other data.
— : Incorrect.
O : Unsubstantiated or unclear.

It was postulated that restricted voice range reflects constriction of normal sexual drives by emotional factors. In the three children where voice range was observed to be restricted, the associated emotional constriction was validated by the clinical data. Breathiness was noted in only one child, and the postulated repression or denial of sexuality was evident in clinical data.

Nasality was observed in three children and harshness in one child. Each of the three where voices were nasal exhibited clinically the passive aggressivity which we postdicted. The one child whose voice was described as harsh was more openly aggressive, and preoccupation with aggression was marked in projective tests.

Clinical Significance of Misarticulated Consonants

Working assumptions six through twelve dealt with the clinical significance of misarticulated consonants, which was postulated as being associated with defensive behavior utilized in establishing relationships with other people. Since articulation of consonants dictates intelligibility of speech, they were felt to reflect satisfactory or unsatisfactory developmental experiences. Here, too, the assumptions appeared to be correct when the speech signs were observed but frequencies of occurrence were in some instances inadequate to make wholly definitive conclusions possible. These data appear in Chart XII.

We note, for example, that the frontal lisp was observed in nine children. Eight of these children were described in other data as maintaining a pregenital level of development, in agreement with our theoretical expectation. In one child where the frontal lisp occurred inconsistently, the data was inconclusive, largely because the child was so difficult to reach in the psychiatric interview that it was nearly impossible to evaluate psychic development. Six children manifested a lateral lisp. All of these children were described by other clinicians as unusually narcissistic.

CHART XII

SYMPTOM FREQUENCY AND ACCURACY OF POSTDICTIONS AS RELATED TO
OBSERVED DEVIATIONS IN THE USE OF CONSONANTS

Name	Frontal Lisp	Lateral Lisp	Whistle	w/r;3	f/θ/	d/ð/	1
1. Sheila:			+		+		
2. Steve:			+				
3. Roddy:	+		+			+	
4. Teddy:		+	+		+		
5. Susan:			+				
6. Gordon:	+		+				
7. Greg:	+		+	w/r +			
8. Terry:	+		+				
9. Darlene:	+		+				
10. Diane:	+		+				
11. Chester:			+				
12. Ray:			(not sustained) +				
13. Sally:	+	+	+		+	+	
14. Vernon:			+		+	+	+
15. Janice:			(not marked) +				
16. Daryl	+	+	+				
17. Vivian:			+	w/r +	+		
18. Rachel:	(inconsistent)0		(inconsistent) +	w/r +			
19. Martin:			(in reading) +	w/r;3: +	+		
20. Lenny:			+				
21. Donald:		+	none +				
22. Karen:		+	" +			+	+
23. Barby:			(Slight, + appropriate)				
24. Ronald:		+	+				

+ : verified.
— : inaccurate.
0 : unclear.

Twenty-three of the twenty-four children examined sometimes articulated the *s* phoneme with an accompanying whistle, though in five children the whistle was infrequent or inconsistent. Postdictions of anxiety in interpersonal relationships were supported by other data in all cases, though individuals varied as to level and source of anxiety. Some were felt to be manifesting appropriate signal anxiety in relation to the examining situation; in others, anxiety appeared to be more deep-seated. Specific postdictions for individual children were given in Chart I and were discussed at some length in the accompanying text (pp. 61-65). The one child, Donald, who did not at any time show a whistling *s* was felt to be atypical in not exhibiting through sound evidence of anxiety. Along with a high pitch, a lateral lisp and some sound rejection, this failure to exhibit the common whistling *s* suggested development in a narcissistic fashion with denial of or conflict about masculinity and identification with the mother. Such an evaluation was in essential agreement with the psychiatrist's picture of the child. In this case, we see the complexly interwoven aspects of speech and the sensitive appraisal required to balance observations.

Four children substituted *w* for *r*, which in our scheme was felt to be an indication of difficulties in interpersonal relationships. Those difficulties appeared in the form of troublesome, demanding, irritating behavior, either overtly manifested in behavior or subtly shown by maneuvers which sabotaged relationships. In each case, these postdictions were supported by other clinical data.

Seven children regularly substituted the *f* phoneme for the voiceless *th* [θ]. This symptom was assumed as being associated with difficulties in the father-child relationship. In all cases, this association was validated in other data. Six of the fathers were unavailable and distant, and in one case (Sally) the father was so overly involved in Sally's early development that problems in the resolution of the oedipal complex and appropriate identification were magnified.

Only two children substituted the phoneme *d* for the voiced *th* [ð], but in each case special difficulties in father-child relationship were present. Each of these children also substituted *f* for the voiceless *th* [θ] with similar associated difficulties in father-child relationships.

Two children misarticulated the *l* phoneme. The postulated

deprivation of early oral needs was verified in these children's clinical records. It can be seen that misarticulation of consonants reflected distorted interpersonal relationships as suggested in each of these working assumptions. However, aside from the almost universal whistling *s*, these signs did not appear with sufficient frequency to allow definitive conclusions though they were so often associated with behavior as postulated that further research would seem worthwhile.

Disturbed Functioning of the Speech Mechanism

Two working assumptions (numbers 13 and 14) were concerned with the clinical significance of disturbed functioning of the speech mechanism. The first of these regarded the tongue thrust, as described and discussed on pp. 45-48, as a reflection of an individual's degree of phallic striving, which could be expected to be present in both boys and girls until the appropriate self-concept is achieved. In the sample of twenty-four children examined, seventeen (eight girls and nine boys) manifested a tongue thrust. In all but one of the girls, and all of the boys, this phenomenon appeared to be correctly associated with masculine striving of some degree. This data is given in Chart XIII. When a tongue thrust appeared in boys who otherwise manifested some disturbance in sexual identification (such as high pitch), the tongue thrust was felt to be a modulating influence in a positive direction. In girls, the presence of a tongue thrust at prepuberty suggested that feminine identification was incomplete or partially conflicted. These assumptions were generally supported by the validating data.

Accuracy of the postdictions of neurological status from quantitative and qualitative observations of diadochokinetic rates was previously discussed (pp. 83-86). Though our validating data was weakest in this area (as indicated in Chart XIII), neurological status appeared to have been correctly assessed by this technique on fifteen of the twenty-three children.

CHART XIII

Symptom Frequency and Accuracy of Postdictions as Related to Observed Deviations in Functioning of the Speech Mechanism

Child	Tongue Thrust	Diadochokinetic Rates
1. Sheila	+	Impaired somewhat +
2. Steve	+	Normal +

CHART XIII (continued

SYMPTOM FREQUENCY AND ACCURACY OF POSTDICTIONS AS RELATED TO
OBSERVED DEVIATIONS IN FUNCTIONING OF THE SPEECH MECHANISM

Child	Tongue Thrust	Diadochokinetic Rates
3. Roddy		Qualitative disturbance +
4. Teddy	+	Normal +
5. Susan	+	Slow +
6. Gordon	+	Normal 0
7. Greg	(mild) +	No comment (probably normal)*
8. Terry		Disturbed 0
9. Darlene	+	Disturbed 0
10. Diane		Normal +
11. Chester	+	Normal +
12. Ray	(mild) +	Disturbed +
13. Sally	+	Normal 0 (aphasic-like difficulties at latency)
14. Vernon		Normal +
15. Janice	+	Qualitatively poor 0
16. Daryl	+	Normal +
17. Vivian	0	Normal +
18. Rachel	+	Normal 0 (problems in perspective)
19. Martin	+	Normal +
20. Lenny	+	Disturbed +
21. Donald	+	Normal 0
22. Karen		Normal +
23. Barby		Normal +
24. Ronald		Disturbed 0

*(Dr. A. Moriarty's remarks)
+ Verifiied.
0 Inconclusive

In eight cases, validating data was inconclusive.

Sound Rejection

Working assumption number fifteen dealt with clinical implications of rejection of sound, as manifested by inability to distinguish auditory stimuli. It was assumed difficulties in distinguishing sounds would reflect behavior comparable to that reflected by misarticulation of the same sounds. Sixteen of the twenty-four children, without organic hearing difficulties, were unable to distinguish one or more sound pairs. In fourteen of the children rejecting sounds, the auditory distortions appeared to reflect some distortion in interpersonal relationships. In two cases, the auditory distortions were not mirrored in other clinical data. Chart XIV shows which children were involved.

CHART XIV

SYMPTOM FREQUENCY AND ACCURACY OF POSTDICTION
AS RELATED TO OBSERVED REJECTION OF SOUND

Child	
1. Sheila	+
2. Steve	+

CHART XIV (continued)

SYMPTOM FREQUENCY AND ACCURACY OF POSTDICTION
AS RELATED TO OBSERVED REJECTION OF SOUND

Child	
3. Roddy	+
4. Teddy	
5. Susan	
6. Gordon	
7. Greg	+
8. Terry	+
9. Darlene	
10. Diane	+
11. Chester	
12. Ray	+
13. Sally	+
14. Vernon	0
15. Janice	+
16. Daryl	+
17. Vivian	
18. Rachel	+
19. Martin	+
20. Lenny	0
21. Donald	+
22. Karen	
23. Barby	
24. Ronald	+

+ Verified.
0 No data.

Speech Defects and Verbal I.Q.

In working assumption number sixteen, we postulated that the presence of a speech defect or dislike for verbal participation would be reflected in low verbal I.Q. as compared to performance I.Q. This assumption was correct for 62 percent of the children. (See Chart IX, pp. 87-90). Special problems interfering with accuracy of this postdiction were discussed on pages 86-87.

Prediction of Earlier Speech Problems

Working assumption number seventeen made the assumption that the presence of disturbances in speech at prepuberty was presumptive of earlier speech problems. Postdictions of this nature were made on fourteen children. Of these, eight were judged as correct, two as incorrect, three as inconclusive because of conflicting data; one as unstable because of lack of evidence. These findings appear in Chart XV.

CHART XV

PRESENCE OF SPEECH DIFFICULTIES WITH PRESUMPTION
OF EARLIER SPEECH DIFFICULTIES

Child		
1. Sheila	±	(Speech development was not slow, but there were numerous articulatory errors at the preschool period.)
2. Steve	±	
3. Roddy	+	
4. Terry		
5. Susan		
6. Gordon		
7. Greg		
8. Terry	+	
9. Darlene	+	
10. Diane	—	
11. Chester		
12. Ray	+	
13. Sally	+	
14. Vernon	+	
15. Janice		
16. Daryl	—	
17. Vivian		
18. Rachel		
19. Martin		
20. Lenny	+	
21. Donald	+	
22. Karen	±	
23. Barby		
24. Ronald	0	

+ Verified.
— Inaccurate.
± Conflicting data.
0 No data.

Chapter VI

Application of the Working Assumptions

In the following pages we wish to present samples of our procedure in using the working assumptions to describe children and in organizing and evaluating the data. We have chosen four children for examples of these processes. These include: (1) Ray, for whom eleven postdictions were made and all were judged correct; (2) Lenny, for whom only half of the postdictions made were judged correct; (3) Vivian, for whom the most postdictions were made and (4) Chester, for whom the least number of postdictions were made. In organizing the raw data available from the speech examination we found it convenient to group it under the headings of *history, anxious reaction to challenge or stress, specific sound difficulties, sound rejection, hearing, residue, voice quality, variability in voice during session, physical observation of speech mechanism, sexual identification, relative skill on verbal and performance scales of the WISC, miscellaneous,* and *summary.* Within each of these sections the data seemed to support certain postdictions. These are recorded in the appropriate place. Following this material we present the material used for the postdiction, the rating of correctness, the validation data and comments about the process where appropriate. Under the columns entitled *validation data* and *comments* the reader will note initials and dates such as (AM, 3/12/54). These symbols indicate the member of the project staff who made the observation and the date on which the observation was made.

The first child we shall consider is Ray for whom the eleven postdictions made were all assessed as correct.

Summary of Speech and Hearing Examination with Postdictions

Ray

Examined 11/14/62, Age 11-11

1. *History:*

   (a.) Ray reported considerable pressure in the speech area between the ages of three and four years when he says he had a "stutter-ing" problem. He was mercilessly teased by his sisters who called him "stutter box." He responded to this by hitting his sisters. He was alternately teased and threatened by his mother who told him she would remove him from kindergarten if he did not improve. He was afraid to show displeasure to the parents. Teasing continued both at home and at school until the age of nine. He remembers no secondary mannerisms or common reaction patterns associated with his stuttering.

(b.) At the present time, Ray enjoys speaking in school and teasing has dropped out completely both at school and at home.

(c.) His mother forces him to sing in the church choir. He dislikes this intensely and is looking forward to the time when he will be too old for the junior choir and not old enough for the adult choir. Postdiction: Since there is no residual evidence of stut-tering and no recall of secondary mannerisms, it is doubtful that Ray ever really stuttered. The family may have misin-terpreted or over-emphasized his tendencies to hesitate and repeat. Nonetheless, there was considerable pressure and tension around speech and communication and this is still present to some extent since the mother feels so strongly about Ray's participation in the choir.

In regard to stuttering mannerisms, one might say either that Ray is a terribly strong denier or that he showed unusual strength in living with his speech difficulties. Probably both are true and particularly the latter. Ray is a basically strong person since he experienced the pressures but tolerated them without collapse and did not develop other symptoms.

2. *Anxious reaction to challenge or stress:*
   Ray has a mild whistling *s* which is not sustained. Postdiction: mild anxiety is present, but it is controlled and not overwhelming.

3. *Specific sound difficulties:*
   Ray speaks fluently with normal articulation and outward confidence. Unusual colloquial speech patterns are superimposed on basically good speech. Postdiction: This would suggest that Ray probably comes from a family of lower socio-economic status.

4. *Sound rejection:*
   Ray showed remarkable and extensive sound rejection. This could occur as a result of either neurological or psychological difficulties.

In most cases, however, he was able to recover. On Form I of the Wepman Test, he failed to differentiate between items 9, 24, 25, 28, 32, and 40. On a second trial he correctly differentiated items 25 and 28. On the third trial he corrected errors on 9, 24, and 32. He was never able to distinguish between the two sounds of item 40. Postdiction: Sound rejection of this extent and the fact that he was never able to discriminate correctly on item 40 suggests an auditory discrimination problem. Ray should have a complete audiological evaluation at the Kansas University Medical Center.

5. *Hearing:*

Ray's hearing is normal except for a loss at 8,000 cycles in the right ear. For this frequency he has a 25 decibel loss. Although such a loss does not present any difficulty in his understanding of speech or language, his hearing should be checked periodically.

Postdiction: Difficulties in discrimination as noted above suggest the possibility of auditory discrimination difficulties which should be checked. Although we have no report by the child to this effect, it seems probable that the mother over the years complained of Ray's ignoring her speech. She might have described him as inattentive or possibly acting as though he were in a world by himself.

6. *Residue:*

(a.) Ray's present voice quality is unusually hoarse. His pitch is too low. This may have resulted from an undue family emphasis on speech and voice, producing a good deal of tension around the ages of three and four, and currently expressed in the mother's insistence on Ray's participation in the choir. Furthermore, we know that Ray has unusual difficulty in differentiating auditory stimuli on the basis of his responses to the Wepman Test. He appears often to pay little attention to the remarks of others and in a sense this may have been an asset, enabling him to withstand the verbal battering he took from family and schoolmates.

In regard to Ray's colloquial speech, we expect that it is generally accepted in the population in which he moves, but it certainly is not elegant. The fact that his present speech is good suggests either that there has been a significant change in family attitude toward the boy or that the teasing actually was not as negative as he perceived it at age three. It may be that the family teased him in terms which sound derogatory but in a context of some warmth.

(b.) Ray's extensive sound rejection suggests that his inability to hear may at times be a logical defense against verbal aggression, particularly from the mother. Apparently she did yell at him a good deal of the time. Postdiction: While there is possibly some indication of cerebral dysfunction as evidenced by his auditory discrimination difficulties, there is also an overlay of psychological defensiveness against the pressures he has experienced.

7. *Voice quality:*
Ray's unusual hoarseness has already been mentioned. We should probably also mention that Ray's singing voice is clear. Postdiction: The nature of Ray's difficulties suggests basic difficulties in sexual identification. The mother apparently demands identification with her and Ray, in his efforts to rush toward masculinity, phonates at a lower pitch than is appropriate. In other words, he tries to overcompensate or overidentify with the father and hence the identification is not comfortable for him. We assume that the mother must be the dominant figure in the family or if she is not dominant then she must be in a vigorous contest with the father for the affection of the children. Since Ray is a basically strong individual, he has over-reacted to this kind of pressure by trying to assume a masculinity which he does not fully feel. Overtly, this appears in his excessively hoarse voice. Another possible interpretation is that he may be hoarse so he will not be able to sing.

8. *Variability in voice quality during session:*
None. The colloquial nature of Ray's speech has already been mentioned. This is excessive, but probably not ordinarily a handicap in his environment.

9. *Physical observation of speech mechanism:*
The peripheral speech mechanism functioned normally. Ray does manifest some tongue thrust but he has no overbite. There are open spaces between his teeth, but this is not particularly significant since he is in the process of acquiring his second teeth. Diadochokinetic rates suggest possible neurological findings. Postdiction: although Ray's speech probably is not considered really bad by most observers, his mild tongue thrust suggests some problems in the area of striving for masculine identification. However, they are not highly pathological since he is not pressing against his teeth to the extent shown in some of the other children in the sample. The qualitative poorness of the diadochokinetic rates for

the *g* phoneme, especially when it is considered along with the 8,000 cycle loss in the right ear and the discrimination problem does suggest possible low-grade neurological findings.

10. *Sexual identification:*

The implications of the speech and hearing evaluation in regard to sexual identification have already been indicated. To reiterate them here: Dr. Rousey postdicts over-reaction on the part of the child to the mother's attempts to get him to identify with her. It almost seems as though the mother is trying to engulf the child. This process is very unsatisfactory to the child and consequently his male identification process is pressured and incomplete.

11. *Relative level of skill on Verbal and Performance Scales of the WISC:*

Postdiction: We would assume that performance scales would exceed verbal scales.

12. *Miscellaneous:*

Ray's colloquial speech patterns are more pronounced than those found in most children. From this we would postdict that Ray comes from a low socio-economic group or that these patterns have evolved as a part of his defensive maneuvers against the mother's pressures in regard to speech and communication.

13. *Summary:*

As we have already indicated, Ray's speech although it is highly colloquial is well within the normal speech patterns of the area in which he lives. The excessive hoarseness in his voice quality may be of physiological origin, but it is equally possible that it has evolved as a vocal reaction to pressure from the mother. In other words, it may be one aspect or overt manifestation of Ray's tendency to over-react to pressure to identify with the mother. Along with these problems there is some indication of difficulty in perceiving some auditory stimuli. While signs of probable neurological malfunction appear definite, they are probably *minimal,* and not grossly incapacitating. Far more impressive is the child's capacity to tolerate psychological pressure and to defend himself against it by over-reacting.

Speech Postdictions and Their Source

Ray

Examined: 1/14/62, Age 11-11

Postdiction

Speech signs, other clinical observations or history contributing to postdictions

1. Ray's reports of his early stuttering must be inaccurate; it seems more likely that normal preschool tendencies to hesitate and repeat were misinterpreted by the family as stuttering.

1. No residue in current speech and no secondary speech mannerisms.

2. He has experienced tension and pressure around speech. This pressure is probably still present and suggests the probability of some deviance in speech functioning.

2. Ray's siblings teased him in the preschool years—calling him "stutterbox." He was teased both at home and at school until about nine years of age. His mother threatened to remove him from kindergarten if his speech did not improve. At present she forces him to sing in the church choir.

3. Ray either has very strong denial tendencies or he has unusual strengths in dealing with speech problems. Probably both these factors play a part in his speech development. The impression of effective adaptation to adverse emotional stimuli is probably reflected in projective tests.

3. He experiences pressure as indicated in item 2, but was able to tolerate this pressure without collapse and did not develop other symptoms. There was either a significant change in family attitude or the pressure was not as negative as it was perceived by the child. Perhaps derogatory comments about his speech were made in the context of warmth.

4. Mild anxiety is present, but it is controlled and not overwhelming.

4. Mild whistling *s*, not sustained.

5. Ray probably comes from a family of lower social-economic status or else his poor

5. In talking, Ray appears to speak confidently and with outward comfort and with

speech results from defensive maneuvers against the mother's pressure in regard to speech and communication.

6. Cortical involvement is strongly suggested by some aspects of the speech evaluations. However these signs are minimal and not grossly incapacitating despite the consistency with which they appear.

7. It is possible that there is some lesion in the auditory pathway.

8. Ray's mother probably described the child as inattentive or as behaving as though he were in a world by himself.

9. Along with neurological factors, there may be an overlay of psychological defensiveness against the pressures he has experienced, particularly

normal articulation. However, unusually colloquial patterns are superimposed on basically good speech.

6. Ray showed remarkable and extensive sound rejection. He failed to differentiate *v* and *th* sounds as in the word pair vow-thou and clothe-clove. Our postdiction is that failure in this discrimination is related to father-son difficulty. Ray also failed to discriminate *f* and *th* as in the word pairs sheaf-sheath and fie-thigh. He also had difficulty discriminating certain vowels, suggesting very early family disturbances. There was a twenty-five decibel loss of hearing in the right ear at 8,000 cycles. Diadochokinetic rates for the *g* phoneme were qualitatively poor.

7. Hearing loss as reported under item 6.

8. Difficulty with discrimination as reported on item 6. This may actually have been an asset in helping him to withstand the verbal battering from his family and schoolmates.

9. Extent of sound rejection. (See item 6)

the verbal aggression from his mother.

10. Ray has basic difficulties in sexual identification. His mother apparently demands identification with her almost to the extent of engulfing the child. Ray in his efforts to rush into masculinity tries to overcompensate or overidentify with the father. Hence identification is pressured and incomplete. The mother must be the dominant member of the family.

10. Unusual hoarseness, too low pitch, mild tongue thrust and clear singing voice.

11. We assume performance scales will exceed verbal scales on the structured tests.

11. The variety of explosive and receptive speech distortions and the history of pressures surrounding speech.

Assessment of Speech Postdictions

Ray
Examined 11/14/62, Age 11-11
Rated by AM, 8/8/63

Validation Data	*Rating*	*Comments*
1. Three-year-old Ray had quite infantile speech with numerous articulatory distortions, but there was no evidence of stuttering in the structured test sessions. (AM, 3/12/54)	5	1. There was in Ray's speech at that time some hesitancy which seemed to reflect confusion in conceptualizing or word finding rather than true stuttering.
2. The slow pace of speech development (single words at nineteen months and sentences at twenty-three months), history of experienced pressures (re-	4	

gardless of the extent to which this was realistic and more recent stories of the mother screaming at the child (once observed by AM) tend to support this postdiction, though perhaps these factors do not fully document it.

3. In the prepuberty TAT record, Ray gave an impression of enjoying life and social contacts in a relatively casual way, seeming to have a positive orientation towards most of his experiences. (AM, 12/10/60) He tries to deny his fears through evasiveness. (PH, 1/21/61) Ray is on the surface cheerful and enthusiastic with an undercurrent of anxiety and fears, rarely expressed, yet he does feel very positive about being alive. (PT, 9/29/63)   5

4. Ray showed some signs of pressure or anxiety which contrasted with his comfortable facade. His practical judgment helps him control anxiety. (PT, 9/29/63)   5

5. There is a slightly rural quality to Ray's speech. (PT, 9/29/63) Ray came from one of the poorest families in the sample.   5   Socio-economic level certainly was verified, but defensiveness may have also been involved here. (See item 8)

(GH, 1/55)

6. There was no mention of possible neurological dysfunctioning in the psychiatric summary, but we know that Ray had a febrile illness with stiffness of the neck in April, 1954.   4

7. Middle ear infection in the second half of the first year. No evidence in history of sensory-neural damage.   4

8. Selective inattention with a tendency to notice little of the physical environment. (PT, 9/29/63)   4

9. Evasiveness reported in the prepuberty Rorschach.   4

10. Ray over-reacts in trying to be manly. His father is somewhat unsatisfactory as an identification figure and the seemingly strong male identification is unsure. "Us men" attitude appears in the way he and the father bypass the mother at times.   5

11. Verbal I.Q., 104—Prepuberty Performance I.Q., 114.   5

Summary

These postdictions appear to be predominantly correct although the assessments were less clear-cut than in some cases due to vagueness in the record. This was probably a function of the failure of Ray's mother to discriminate in her memories between her children.

The effectiveness of Ray's coping strategies strikes me (Dr.

Moriarty) as quite impressive. On the one hand he has been able to rebel, but he has done so in such a mild fashion that he does not risk overstepping the conformity expected of him. It seems to me that he has used his mild neurological handicap in a way which is essentially positive in enabling him to maintain his own equilibrium. Furthermore, I suspect that reports of early stuttering probably reflected the usual hesitations and repetitions one hears in the speech of a preschool child. They were undoubtedly intensified by the mother's concern and certainly did create pressure for the child in this area. It was interesting to me that Dr. Rousey did not see any residue of the markedly infantile speech nor did Ray himself recall anything about the nature of the many substitutions we observed in his three-year-old speech. In other words, Ray appears to have remembered the pressures in trying to communicate and be understood rather than the exact nature of the difficulty as we observed it. I agree with Dr. Rousey that the most impressive aspect of Ray as an individual is his strength in tolerating pressure and his capacity to use the equipment he has most effectively. If problems appear in the future, I should expect that faulty and pressured sex identification would be more handicapping to his future development than his mild neurological deficit. The neurological difficulties very possibly did contribute to slow rate of cognitive development and to the mild fluctuating pattern we saw on the structured tests. Ray's capacity to ignore or deny may have been psychically economical, but at the same time they probably also deprived and will continue to deprive him of full mobilization of and gratification from potentially good intellectual ability. He may not be as bright as his older brother Charles, but the chances are that the discrepancy in potential ability is not as great as might be indicated by the quantitative results of the tests given him over the years.

The next example is Lenny for whom only 50 percent of the postdictions made were judged correct.

Summary of Speech and Hearing Examination with Postdictions

Lenny

Examined 12/18/62, Age 11-7

1. *History:*

Facts in the case history on this child underlined Dr. Rousey's impression of anxiety and fright which permeated the speech and hearing test. Although Lenny was overtly cooperative, it was very obvious that the tests made him uneasy. His use of speech and verbal processes was deviant throughout the session.

Lenny reported that he was given speech therapy during the first and second grade. He did not know or could not remember the exact nature of his speech difficulty, but the impact of these experiences was suggested by the fact that he momentarily lost his voice while talking about his early speech problems.

In the fourth grade, Lenny's hearing was tested as a result of a teacher's complaint that he seemed not to hear well. At the end of the examination he was told that he had better hearing than the teacher.

At the present time, Lenny reported that he hears sounds in his ears sometimes, occurring in relation to being accidentally hit, as by a ball. He described the sounds as being like the dying vibrations of a piece of tin which has been struck. He thinks that this occurs about once a month. Apparently he has not discussed this with his parents. Postdiction: These facts suggest a deviant or unhealthy resistance to sound intake. Apparently there is some psychological basis for denying, shutting out or rejecting what he hears in order to protect himself and preserve his equilibrium. There may have been other somatic symptoms appearing at the time of the fourth grade hearing tests or he may have been undergoing some special crisis at that time. Currently, he seems to attempt to solve his problems by denying and withdrawing.

2. *Anxious reaction to challenge or stress:*

There was a prominent whistle present most of the time although this disappeared occasionally giving an intermittent effect. He has difficulties pronouncing a great many words, as one might observe in stuttering, but this sometimes disappears. Occasionally he lost his voice, most notably so when he was reading sentences. He apparently has trouble sustaining an ability to phonate.

3. *Specific sound difficulties:*

Lenny has trouble with double and triple consonant blends. He also tends to omit the final sound. He was able to correct these errors when he was stimulated to do so. In some respects this is characteristic of the speech of a retarded child, but we should not expect a retarded child to be able to make the corrections as Lenny did. Therefore we would not expect Lenny to be retarded. Lenny made both qualitative and quantitative errors in producing the *s* sound.

4. *Sound rejection:*

He was never able to distinguish between the discrimination pairs, lave-lathe or wreathe-reef. In a number of discrimination pairs he took an unusually long time to judge similarities and differences. This was particularly impressive since with thirty other discrimination pairs he was able to make an immediate choice as to similarity or difference. The combinations with which he had trouble were the following: sake-shake, ball-ball, lake-lake, lit-lick, lass-lath, fret-threat, bar-bar, bum-bun, vie-thy. These failures to discriminate were particularly impressive in view of the fact that Lenny's hearing was normal. Hence we would postdict that he probably has had difficulties in attending and comprehending in school.

5. *Hearing:*
Normal.

6. *Residue:*

The poor speech at the present time suggests that Lenny probably had early speech difficulties which were quite marked and persisted longer than expected in the average young child. His family and associates must have been aware of these difficulties.

7. *Voice quality:*

Lenny has unusual difficulty in phonating. He seems to have periodic loss of control over his voice which suggests that he lacks a stable self-concept. This must have been present at a very early age and is still in evidence.

8. *Variability in voice quality during session:*

Although Lenny's speech was in general very poor, the pronounced whistle was intermittent and there were periods in which the voice was lost all together. The intensity of Lenny's speech problems combined with this kind of variability suggests that speech is a highly pressured area for him.

9. *Physical observation of speech mechanism:*

Lenny has both a tongue thrust and overbite. He also showed qualitative difficulties in his diadochokinetic rates on the phonemes of *d* and *g*. We would postdict some neurological background.

10. *Sexual identification:*

Sexual identification is primarily feminine, or at least he has strong tendencies toward feminine behavior. Such an impression was fortified to some extent by the fact that he looked mildly feminine in appearance and had difficulty maintaining phonation. Identification with his father will probably continue to be an area of pressure and conflict for him for some time.

11. *Relative level of skill on verbal and performance scales of the WISC:*
We postdict relatively higher performance scores than verbal scores.

12. *Miscellaneous:*
Nothing additional.

13. *Summary:*
Lenny's conscious uneasiness in speech functioning is reflected by his periodic loss of control over phonation, his peculiar variations in diadochokinetic rates and his persistent whistling *s*. His difficulties in differentiating between similar or different words is highly atypical. His failure to handle incoming sound stimuli adequately despite normal hearing raises the question of possible hysterical factors in his development. More serious however is the fact that he tends to hear sounds which are not there. He's trying to handle his difficulties by staying on guard and will probably become more schizoid as he grows older.

Speech Postdictions and Their Source

Lenny
Examined 12/18/62, Age 11-7

Postdiction	*Speech signs, other clinical observations, or history contributing to postdictions*
1. Lenny has a deviant or unhealthy resistance to sound intake. Apparently there is some psychological basis for denying, shutting out or rejecting what he hears in order to protect himself and preserve his equilibrium.	1. Uneasiness throughout the session; deviant use of speech; loss of voice while telling about early speech problems and while reading; reported sounds in his ears. Prominent whistle, though somewhat intermittent.
2. Lenny probably experiences difficulty in attending and comprehending in school.	2. Many qualitative and quantitative errors in producing *s* sound. Never able to discriminate between the word pairs lave-lathe or wreathe-reef. He took an unusually

3. Probably Lenny had marked and persistent speech difficulties as a young child.

4. Lenny has an unstable self-concept. It is probable that this was true from an early age and it definitely is still in evidence.

5. Speech and communication are highly pressured areas.

6. There may be a neurological background to Lenny's speech difficulties.

7. Sexual identification is primarily feminine or mixed with strong tendencies toward feminine behavior. Efforts to identify with the father create pressure and conflict which undoubtedly will be evident for some time.

8. Lenny probably does better on performance tests than on verbal tests.

9. It is possible that hysterical factors are involved in Lenny's development.

10. He handles difficulties by staying on guard and may become more schizoid as he grows older.

long time to judge similarities and difficulties. He does have normal hearing.

3. Poor present speech.

4. Difficulties in phonating, periodic loss of control of voice.

5. Generally poor speech with intermittent whistle, loss of voice and variability in quality of speech.

6. Diadochokinetic rate disturbances with *d* and *g* phonemes.

7. Sound discrimination difficulties as described under item 2, fortified by mildly feminine appearance and disturbance in maintaining phonation.

8. Seriousness of his present speech difficulties.

9. Lenny fails to handle incoming stimuli adequately despite normal hearing. He hears sounds that are not present.

10. Delay in responding on discrimination test.

Assessment of Speech Postdictions

Lenny
Examined 12/18/62, Age 11-7
Rated by AM, 8/19/63

Validation Data	*Rating*	*Comments*
1. Auditory stimulation is less meaningful to Lenny than visual stimulation. (PT, 12/57) Lenny is making good progress in handling "developmental learning difficulties"; emotional factors are minimally involved. (JS, 9/60)	3	1. Neurological factors (as reported in item 6) probably outweighed psychological factors. His hearing, though not impaired, was subject to distortion in his early years through repeated infections. (PS, 6/61)
2. He is not doing too well in school. (PT, 6/15/62) On the Stanford-Achievement Test (AM, 6/62) he obtained an overall grade placement of 5.9 at the end of his 6th year of elementary school. Arithmetic and spelling achievements fell below this level, reading and social studies above it.	4	2. Lenny has considerable real visual handicaps, but in spite of this he does quite well, and tries hard though he can easily get discouraged. A quality of irritability, notable in the earlier sessions, has become increasingly controlled, especially in sympathetic and supportive situations. (AM, 12/57)
3. At three and one-half years, Lenny had very infantile speech. At age seven, speech was much improved though his voice was husky, tones slurred and many articulatory errors were observed. He had trouble with word-finding and sentence structure was often awkward. However, he was ingenious in offering substitute explanations, often quite vivid and poetic in nature. (AM, 3/58)	5	
4. Lenny is keenly aware of his shortcomings, but he	2	

strives vigorously to over-
come them and his efforts
are so efficient that he
does compensate for some
of them. He has much
self-doubt, but he is quite
comfortable with himself.
His aspirations for the
future are somewhat un-
real and in some ways he
is insecure, yet he deals
with this with strength
and resourcefulness. (PT,
12/57)

5. Lenny covers his mouth   5
and speaks softly; he is
more comfortable in ex-
pressing himself through
movement.

6. Certain organic difficul-   5   6. JS's summary of his ex-
ties are hinted at by his   amination with Lenny in
poor speech. His spatial   1957 reported scarring of
orientation is somewhat   the eardrums bilaterally,
poor and he has trouble   divergent strabismus of
in estimating relative sizes   the left eye, deformity of
of things. He seems to   the optic nerve head. At
have mild, non-specific   that time J.S. diagnosed
brain damage. (PT,   Lenny as having develop-
12/57)   mental aphasia, predom-
                                          inantly motor type.

7. Lenny is most attached   2   7. Failure in this postdiction
to his mother, but he also   suggests a need to clarify
has strong positive rela-   very specifically exactly
tionships with his father,   what is meant by sexual
even though his love and   identification. It occurs
admiration for his father   to me that warmth of
are mixed with some crit-   attachment to the mother
icism. Identification is   has been confused with
primarily with the father.   identification.
(PT, 6/15/62) Mascu-
line identification is well

advanced despite traits of passivity associated with his dependent compliant needs. (PH, 6/61)

8. Prepuberty WISC—
VIQ = 104, PIQ = 110.

    4

8. The difference appeared in the direction indicated, but quantitative difference was minimal and may not be of great significance.

9. Though there are some signs of immaturity and impulsivity in the Rorschach test as of 6/61 and 6/63, this is largely balanced by control, constructive use of distancing and reality testing. (AM, 6/63)

    2

9. Although hearing does not appear to be impaired in present hearing tests, numerous infections during the early years must have distorted sound intake.

10. There are subtle expressions of approach and withdrawal, of diffused tension release, alternating with moments of composure—all indicating quite a sensitive level of interaction. (LBM, 6/15/62) Lenny was more distant in 6/62 than I had experienced him before, but this seemed to be in relation to feelings surrounding the paternal grandparents' divorce rather than a change in general attitude towards the observers. In a sense, he maintained some reserve in regard to sharing problems he considered personal. (AM notes)

    2

10. In my estimation, the sensitivity and warmth Lenny is able to show in relation to human interaction outweigh his tendencies to withdraw. (AM, 6/63) He has always been able to evade, but on the whole he uses avoidance constructively. (AM, 3/58)

Summary

It seems to me (Dr. Moriarty) that the present postdictions have gone astray to some extent through overemphasis on problems without enough weight given to Lenny's adaptability, social charm and without regard to his current age level. On the whole he has seemed to make a better adjustment to multiple physical handicaps than is indicated in the CR predictions. From my viewpoint, Lenny is a strong individual with more resilience and adaptability than the current postdictions suggest. The obsessiveness, distancing and withdrawal which do appear both in the speech evaluation and in projective tests seems to be more than balanced by Lenny's capacity to enjoy and his sensitive awareness of how much self-control is needed to stay within reality bounds and to accomplish what he sets out to do. (AM, 6/63)

Of the ten postdictions made, five were rated essentially correct and five as essentially incorrect.

The largest number of postdictions (13) were made on Vivian. 62 percent of these postdictions were judged to be correct.

Summary of Speech and Hearing Examination with Postdictions

Vivian

Examined 12/4/62, Age 10-3

1. *History:*

Vivian reported no history of speech difficulties in herself or her family. While she reported that she likes to talk in school and has a real interest in speaking out, she seemed so constrained in her action that one felt this capacity represented her wishes and fantasies rather than reality. She also reported that she sucked her thumb up to nine years of age at which point she stopped. In the context of her present appearance and behavior, one might assume that thumb sucking if it occurred was not of the usual type, that is, not that of a vigorous thumb sucker but perhaps a gentle and passive maneuver which was certainly not nurturant and probably tactile in form of gratification. At the present time, Vivian is taking exercises to correct tongue thrust.

Part of the rationale for such exercise is based on the assumption that bottle fed babies sometimes develop poor swallowing habits, resulting in pushing the tongue forward rather than backward in the course of swallowing. In an effort to correct this, the child is directed to hold something like a life-saver or a button with the tongue against the hard palate. In other cases, mechanical bars are placed in the back of the mouth to control tongue movements. There is some question whether there is in reality a transfer from passive retention of the tongue by such means to control of tongue movements which are exceedingly rapid in the course of normal speech. Especially in a mild passive child like Vivian such procedures may have psychological overtones which are definitely unfortunate to say the least.

2. *Anxious reaction to challenge or stress:*
Vivian showed a definite whistle, occurring on the formal speech tests under the pressure of probing questions. This situation worsened as the evaluation proceeded. Postdiction: Vivian's defense mechanisms and forms of adjustment appeared to be paper thin and are easily cracked. This showed through in her exceedingly soft voice almost at the level of a whisper. Both the whistle and the exceedingly soft voice reflect some weakness in her ability to react to any stress-inducing situation particularly when the person with whom she is in contact is perceived as older, as having more status or prestige. Almost any life situation could be expected to aggravate this condition.

3. *Specific sound difficulties:*
Along with the whistle as described above, Vivian substitutes *f* for the voiceless *th* sound and *w* for *r*. Postdiction: The *f* for *th* substitution reflects difficulties in the development of a self-concept related to the lack of a strong father figure in the picture. He either is not or was not available as a factor in her affective development. The *w* for *r* substitution suggests passive aggressive tendencies such that she would be expected to be a troublemaker in school not in terms of violent acting out but rather in terms of neutral obstructionist tactics. She probably is not overtly negativistic but she might be considered very frustrating to a teacher since she does have excessive difficulties in giving of herself or expressing her feelings and ideas. The teacher may be unable to pin down reasons for concern about Vivian but these concerns are probably present in a vague general sense.

4. *Sound rejection:*
There is no evidence of sound rejection. In other words, there is no difficulty with the intake of sound. However, one would postdict

that Vivian probably does better in school on nonverbal activities such as mathematics or in subject matter which does not involve relating to people. In the present test, the items of discrimination were relatively neutral. If they had been emotionally laden, there probably would have been some indication of rejection.

5. *Hearing:*
Normal.

6. *Residue:*
The soft speaking voice does not appear to be a residue of early speech problems, but along with the sound substitution seems to reflect an early failure to develop an adequate self-concept.

7. *Voice quality:*
Vivian's intensity of phonation deviates from the normal in its extremely soft, whispered-like quality. Postdiction: One would guess either that Vivian was and continues to be severely restricted emotionally or else that the emotional environment in which she grew was somehow lacking. In other words the parents appeared not to have had the capacity to provide the child with a healthy emotional environment. The amount and kind of constriction seen in Vivian's present behavior suggests that it is most likely that her early environment was extremely restricted.

8. *Variability and voice quality during session:*
We have already noted that the whistle became increasingly worse as the session proceeded. As indicated above, this leads to a postdiction of a superficial kind of life adjustment which is exceedingly vulnerable to stress and easily cracked.

9. *Physical observation of speech mechanism:*
Vivian has a tongue thrust and an overbite. Diadochokinetic rates were normal, negating the postdiction of neurological findings. The rest of her speech mechanism was also considered within the normal range. Postdiction: In a family as severely restricting as Vivian's, her only possible way of identification is in a masculine sense. This however is not tolerated by her parents and she has to inhibit it, hence she hits against the upper teeth in a fashion causing a mild malocclusion.

10. *Sexual identification:*
It seems apparent that Vivian never really had a strong identification as a person to say nothing of a sex identification. She has not really reached an appropriate level of identification on a sexual basis and her preliminary efforts in a masculine direction have been thwarted.

11. *Relative level of skill on verbal and performance scales of the WISC:* One would postdict a higher performance scale I.Q. than verbal scale I.Q.

12. *Miscellaneous:*
The examiner experienced unusual difficulty in conversing with this child. This, however, seemed not so much to be a reflection of difficulties arising from the immediate situation as difficulties arising from longtime problems in relating to almost anyone. Her inhibited verbal expressiveness may reflect an anal retentive pattern of behaving which one would expect to show up as a predominant theme on the projective tests.

13. *Summary:*
Vivian was seen as a highly vulnerable child, who unless she is quite sheltered throughout her life may run into intense psychological trouble as she meets the ordinary stresses of adolescence, marriage and so on. If she is to become a fully effective adult, treatment is probably indicated. There is a special difficulty here insofar as she feels she is more capable in self-expression particularly in school than is actually the case. It would not be unlikely for her to develop hysterical symptoms. One might also see some form of displacement of her feelings and conflicts into physical complaints.

Speech Postdictions and Their Source
Vivian

Examined: 12/4/62, Age 10-3

Speech signs, other clinical observations, or history contributing to postdictions

Postdictions

1. Vivian's reported skills in communication probably represent her wishes or fantasies rather than realistic fact.

1. The extent of constraint and extreme softness of her voice.

2. Vivian's defense mechanisms and forms of adjustment appeared to be paper-thin and easily cracked. She probably is exceedingly uncomfortable in any stress-inducing situation, particularly if the indi-

2. Definite whistle on formal speech tests under the pressure of probing questions. Very soft, almost whispered speech.

vidual with whom she is in contact is perceived as older, as having more prestige or status. Almost any life situation probably aggravates or elicits tension.

3. There are difficulties in the development of a strong self-concept related to lack of a strong father-figure. The father was and is either not available or somehow too inconsistent to be useful to Vivian as a factor in her affective development.

4. Vivian has passive-aggressive tendencies and possibly shows neutral obstructionist tactics. Probably she is not overtly negative, but she may be very frustrating to those in contact with her since she has excessive difficulties in giving of herself or expressing her feelings and ideas. Her teachers are probably concerned about her in a vague, general sense.

5. Vivian probably does better in school in non-verbal activities; she might excel in math or in subjects which involve less relationship to people.

6. Vivian is severely constricted emotionally or her affective environment has been lacking in some respects. Probably Vivian's parents failed to provide a completely healthy emotional environ-

3. Whistle; substitution of *f* for voiceless *th* sound; speech of low intensity.

4. *W* for *r* substitution.

5. Speech of low intensity. No sound rejection, but this might have occurred if discrimination pairs had been less neutral and more affect-loaded.

6. Extremely soft voice and a constraint in action.

ment or they overly restricted her.

7. Negative neurological findings.

8. Vivian's preliminary efforts towards identification are in a masculine direction but her parents inhibit this.

9. Vivian experiences extreme difficulties in relating to people; this is not specific to the present situation but of long-standing nature. She has never had strong identity as a person, to say nothing of sexual identification. She does not reach any level of sexual identification since her preliminary efforts in a masculine direction have been thwarted.

10. Anal-retentive behavior patterns probably appear in the projective tests.

11. We anticipate higher performance than verbal scale I.Q.

12. Vivian is a highly vulnerable child. One would anticipate intense psychological difficulties as she meets the ordinary stresses of adolescence, marriage and so on. Treatment is indicated.

13. Hysterical symptoms may appear in so far as she may displace her feelings and conflicts into physical complaints.

7. Normal speech mechanism and diadochokinetic rates.

8. Tongue thrust and overbite. Vivian is currently taking exercises to correct this.

9. Unusual difficulty in carrying on a conversation with the examiner.

10. Extreme inhibition in verbal expressiveness.

11. Extreme inhibition in the use of speech.

12. Vivian has an unrealistic assumption as to her capacity for self-expression, especially in view of the intensity of inhibition observed in her verbal expressiveness.

13. Verbal passivity and inability to achieve self-expression.

Assessment of Speech Postdictions

Vivian

Examined 12/14/62, Age 10-3

Rated by AM, 8/15/63

Validation Data	Rating	Comments
1. Vivian often volunteers to answer questions the teacher asks, but she rarely smiles and shows little pleasure with praise. She also speaks very softly, sometimes almost inaudibly. (JM, 12/13/60)	4	1. Vivian's responsiveness in school seems to be a part of her passivity and the quite rigid structure; that is, she conforms but without much sign of pleasure.
2. Vivian faints at the sight of blood and gets upset when other children are hurt. (MF, 9/1/61) She is frightened of dogs and scarey movies. (PT, 8/10/62) She struggles with resistance to her negative feelings, coming up with timid, barely formed percepts. When she allows herself some spontaneity, tension increases. (PH, 5/13/61)	4	2. Many situations are tension-arousing for Vivian. However, she is so successful in avoiding feelings and interactions that it seems unlikely that she will break down but rather settle for a dull, inflexible kind of conformity.
3. Whenever Vivian was asked for decisions, it seemed as though she had not "the faintest idea as to what she might think or feel." (PT, 8/10/62) She sees herself as a shy, quiet little girl who is anxious about the environment but in a diffuse way since she is not much aware of it. She longs for her father, but	5	

he is too busy to be much available and Vivian indicates that he does not like children very well. (PT, 8/10/62)

4. Vivian probably never takes the initiative in anything she does. In her own passive way, she sometimes manages to rebel, as by banging doors, but her anger sounds frustrated and impotent. With PT she was comparatively uncommunicative, giving little information about herself. (PT, 8/10/62) Vivian missed a month of school during May and April, 1961. No physical basis for her incessant crying was found. Her teacher was very concerned and tried to help but with little success. (JS, 10/61)

    5

5. This was not true in terms of her grades, as of 1960, the last date for which we have school data. However, grade placement on the Scholastic Achievement Test given at school was higher in arithmetic than in reading or religion.

    3   5. Data were not clear-cut and were for an earlier period.

6. Vivian shows massive repression of all unacceptable feelings. She has been disappointed in

    5   6. At the time of the preschool contact, Vivian shared a bedroom with her father, while her sis-

relationships with both parents particularly the father who is distant. She has some warmth from her mother, but she does not get as much attention as she wants.

7. No mention was made of any neurological problems in the physical or psychiatric evaluations or could be inferred from the psychological tests.   5

8. "Counterphobic reaction to a concern over her own lack of masculinity." (PH, 5/13/61)   4

9. Vivian has just a few close friends, but her relationships are mainly with her sisters. She has identified with her mother despite the envy she has of her brother. (PT, 8/10/62)   3

10. Vivian shows vagueness and constriction in expressiveness and in the quality of her percepts. (PH, 5/13/61) Possessions are very meaningful to Vivian. She is neat and conscientious in carrying out assigned tasks. She does not give much of herself. (PT, 8/10/62)   4

11. Prepuberty WISC, VIQ = 109, PIQ = 106   1

ter Daryl slept with her mother. A younger brother slept sometimes at home and sometimes next door with his grandparents. (GH, 1955)

9. It is probably true that forming relationships is a very difficult task for Vivian, but she seems to have advanced further in identification with her mother than CR's prediction suggests.

11. Vivian appeared to enjoy the structured tests and was on the whole less inhibited than her sister.

12. Vivian is a psychologically colorless child who shuts out the unpleasant by massive repression. She lives in a microcosmic world but appears to accept her lot as inevitable without much regret. The outlook for her future is relatively good **unless** adolescence plays havoc with repression.

2

12. Both PT and CR see Vivian as extremely inhibited, but PT appears to feel that the child's resignation makes her less vulnerable than she is seen by CR.

13. In April and May of 1961, Vivian missed about one month of school with an undiagnosed illness. She cried frequently without apparent reason. (PS, 10/21/61)

3

13. We might assume a hysterical basis for this illness but the assumption can not be proved or disproved on the basis of this data.

Summary

This record was one of the most difficult to assess and certainly one where there was more question about the accuracy of the postdictions. Partly, this was a function of the child's vagueness and incapacity to reveal much of herself. Comparing Dr. Rousey's impressions with those of PT's, it seems as though Dr. Rousey may have been swayed by the extensive repression whereas PT saw her as equally restricted but less vulnerable because of the quality of resignation.

Of thirteen postdictions, eight were accurate or predominantly accurate; two were inaccurate or predominantly inaccurate and three were doubtful or not verifiable.

The fewest postdictions (7) were made on Chester; of these 86 percent were judged to be correct.

Summary of Speech and Hearing Examination with Postdictions

Chester
Examined: 11/27/62, Age 13-7
11-27-62

1. *History:*
   Chester gave no history of early speech difficulties. He did, however, confirm the speech troubles as reported by his brother Ray. Chester placed Ray's difficulty in time as beginning after the possible polio episode. He said that mother, father and older sisters teased Ray a great deal. He did not mention that he himself teased his brother. He described Ray's difficulties as a kind of "dutchy" speech, a sort of a stutter.

2. *Anxious reaction to challenge or stress:*
   Chester showed a definite whistle evoked by stress on the examiner's part. We would postdict anxiety in relation to stress.

3. *Specific sound difficulties:*
   Nothing in addition to the whistling *s*.

4. *Sound rejection:*
   None.

5. *Hearing:*
   The hearing tests given in grade school and most recently in seventh grade indicated no hearing problems. There was no history of hearing difficulties in the family. In the present audiometric evaluation, Chester showed a loss at the frequencies of 1,000 cps, 2,000 cps, and 4,000 cps. This occurred only in the right ear. In regard to this, Chester remarked that he thinks he hears better in the right ear. He complains of pressures in his right ear which he thinks originated last summer following a time when he was kicked in the ear while swimming. Postdiction: His description of better hearing in the right ear is not what would be expected in terms of his audiogram. Such a hearing loss might result in difficulties in localizing sound in a group. It seems possible that such a hearing loss might be a defensive maneuver, perhaps related to an occasional wish to remove himself from the noisiness or confusion of his large family. However, adequate facilities for testing this assumption were not available.

6. *Residue:*
   See Item 7.

7. *Voice quality:*
   Chester has an unusually hoarse and intense voice suggesting active conflict about the necessity of growing up too soon. The hoarseness may be a residue of his unsuccessful efforts to identify with his father too soon. Vocally, this conflict appears through his phonating at too low a pitch. In addition, Chester has a restricted pitch range.

From this we would postdict that he is capable of functioning at a higher emotional level than he achieves. One would anticipate evidences of such constriction in the Rorschach protocol.

8. *Variability in voice quality during session:*
Chester's voice was fairly consistent throughout the evaluation session.

9. *Physical observation of speech mechanism:*
Chester showed a tongue thrust without an overbite. Diadocho-kinetic rates were normal, negating a postdiction of neurological findings. Postdiction: There are in Chester's speech manifestations of phallic strivings which he does not inhibit. Probably they are going on at an inappropriately fast pace if we are to judge from his voice quality.

10. *Sexual identification:*
Chester's sexual identification is basically masculine but is proceeding too rapidly, forcing him to assume adult masculinity too quickly. In this, Chester and his brother Ray are alike. Probably in both cases the combination of a dominant mother and a passive father are etiologically significant.

11. *Relative level of skill on verbal and performance scales of the WISC:*
We postdict higher performance than verbal scales, especially since he seems to prefer and be more comfortable with men. It appears that he can talk to men more easily and it might be that cognitive functioning would be more effective in the presence of men. This could be checked by referring to his school achievement with male and female teachers. On the basis of his speech patterns, we would postdict that Chester would obtain better grades with male teachers.

12. *Miscellaneous:*
Nothing additional.

13. *Summary:*
Chester has a distinct tendency toward adopting physical symptoms as a way of expressing conflict. This may be a result of his family structure, specifically the parental relationships in which the mother appears to be dominant. Chester is currently struggling to achieve a male sexual identity and this may be the origin of his present anxiety.

Speech Postdictions and Their Source

Chester
Examined: 11/27/62, Age 13-7

Speech Postdictions	*Speech signs, other clinical observations or history contributing to postdictions*
1. He was anxious in relation to stress from the examiner.	1. Whistle.
2. The presence of some hearing loss appears to be a defensive maneuver related to occasional wishes to remove himself from the noisiness or confusion of his large family. He may have a tendency toward adopting physical symptoms as a way of expressing conflict.	2. Chester has a hearing loss at frequencies of 1,000, 2,000, and 4,000 in the right ear. He complained of pressures in his right ear, presumably originating last summer when he was kicked in this ear while swimming. In spite of this he feels he hears better in this ear than in the left ear.
3. Chester is in active conflict about growing up too soon and is making unsuccessful efforts to identify with the father too rapidly.	3. His voice is unusually hoarse and tense. He phonates at too low a pitch. His voice quality is restricted in range suggesting unnecessary psychological constrictions.
4. Phallic strivings are not inhibited, but are proceeding at an inappropriately rapid pace.	4. He has a tongue thrust without an overbite.
5. His sexual identification is basically masculine, but it is developing too rapidly, forcing him to assume adult masculinity too quickly. We assume that his efforts toward male identification are complicated by his relationships to a dominant mother and passive father.	5. A combination of the signs reported under items 3 and 4.
6. Performance scale is probably higher than verbal scale on the structured tests.	6. There is a restriction in range of voice quality and some disturbance in speech patterns.

7. Chester is probably more comfortable with men than with women. Cognitive functioning is perhaps more effective with men; this should show up in better grades when he has male teachers.

7. Combination of items 3 and 4.

Assessment of Postdictions

Chester
Examined: 11-27-62, Age 13-7
Rated by AM, 8/8/63

Validation Data	*Rating*	*Comments*
1. Chester was very serious in the psychiatric examination, even sometimes a little pained; the interview seemed to be a definite strain on him. There are a number of underlying anxieties, for the most part carefully denied and repressed. (PT, 11/3/61)	5	
2. Chester has intense feelings about the size of his family and considerable ambivalence in relating to individual members. (PT, 11/3/61) The scatter on the prepuberty WISC is "suggestive of a hysterically organized person." (MM, Conference, 12/17/62)	4	2. The ambivalence about his family is quite clear in a number of records, but reference to possible hysterical organization appeared only once, and this was followed by some reservations.
3. Chester deliberately curbs his interests in order to live within current family situations. He has a lively imagination, but his fan-	5	

tasy must serve a purpose. He appeared to be somewhat inhibited emotionally, but underneath this facade he showed a rich and modulated emotional life. He is reluctant to grow up because more will be expected of him. He is unhappy about an insufficient amount of childish dependency allowed him by his mother. He probably also inhibits energy output because of a need to suppress conflicting feelings. (PT, 11/3/61) Emotional expression is inhibited and he identifies with adult aims in an exaggerated way. (PH, Conference, 11/26/62)

4. Identification with the father may be too strong at prepuberty so that he may settle for a lower role than he can actually handle. (JM reporting at TM's evaluation Conference, 11/26/62)

5. Chester has made a good identification as reflected in his interests in general attitude, but in identifying with his father, he has also identified with his father's inability to dominate the home. He gives "the impression that

4

5

it really is the mother who wears the pants in the family." (PT, 11/3/61)

6. Prepuberty WISC: 3
   Verbal I.Q. 118
   Performance I.Q. 120
   Latency WISC:
   Verbal I.Q. 116
   Performance I.Q. 104

6. This postdiction is accurate as of prepuberty but the discrepancy is not very great. At latency, this relationship was reversed, although Chester was more comfortable with the performance test and one might have anticipated higher scores on the performance items.

7. Chester perceived one   5
   particular female teacher as a castrating figure. (PT, 11/3/61) He denies and avoids too close relationships with his mother and with women in general. (AM, Latency CAT summary, 3/20/61). JM (Conference, 12/7/62) reported that Chester makes better grades with male teachers.

Summary

Five postdictions were fully documented in other data. One postdiction concerning hysterical organization of personality structure was hypothesized on the basis of structured test pattern at prepuberty, but this was not entirely clear-cut. The only postdiction which was not supported by any other data was that in regard to expected higher performance scores than verbal scores on structured tests. While the performance scores were higher, the discrepancy was too slight to allow much weight to be placed on it. However, greater ease on performance tests suggested some tendency in this direction, perhaps overweighted by intellectualizing tendencies which became more prominent in prepuberty.

Chapter VII

Summary and Implications

THE PRESENT report should be regarded as a pilot study of the hypothesis that the manner and quality of expressing and perceiving individual speech sounds reflect psychologically meaningful aspects of human functioning and behavior. Quite apart from universal or idiosyncratic symbolic associations of sound groupings of formal languages, analysis of the form and quality of verbal speech and hearing provides a new and dynamically significant way of understanding some major aspects of communication between the experienced self and the interpersonal environment. Specifically, parameters of speech, such as voice quality, rate, intensity, pitch, accuracy or deviance in articulation, and psychological receptivity of sound appear to be related to personality development and mental health. In essence, structural aspects of the use of sound are self-expressive insofar as behavior in the speech and hearing evaluation offers projective cues of ways and manner of relating to and interacting with other individuals. In this sense, such an examination in the hands of a skillful examiner can be used to complement and supplement the usual psychological tests as it throws light on an individual's orientation to the world, the intensity and mobilization of his basic sexual and aggressive drives, and his competence in relating to others.

Encouraged by professional colleagues the authors conceived and developed seventeen specific working assumptions. These assumptions were then studied in relation to the speech and hearing behavior of twenty-four prepuberty-aged children from a normal sample intensively studied for more than a decade. Our conceptualization of the dynamic implications of speech is the integration of professional experiences, observations and reading, extensive theoretical thinking and experimental evidence in the areas of speech, language, linguistics, audiology, neurology and clinical psy-

chology. Some of this material has been summarized in the first
two chapters of this paper.

Our examining procedures included a brief interview with each
child concerning his view of his own speech development and
capacity for verbal communication; measurement of auditory sensitivity by a pure tone audiometer; auditory discrimination of common
speech sounds as they occur in initial, medial or final positions in
words as given in the Wepman Auditory Discrimination Test;
examination of the peripheral speech mechanism, i.e., structural
aspects of the oral apparatus and quantitative and qualitative
functioning of diadochokinesis; and oral reading of sentences from
the Templin-Darley Tests of Articulation.

Findings from these tests were summarized for each subject.
These summaries were then culled for postdictions relevant to the
working assumptions. Unfortunately, for research purposes, it was
not possible to make postdictions for each child in regard to each
working assumption since the postdictions depended on the presence
of distortions or deviations in the use of speech. Where the speech
symptom was not present, one could not necessarily assume that the
child was free from conflict. For example, when hoarseness was
observed (eight cases), the postdiction was made that sexual identification would be distorted. The lack of observed hoarseness in the
other children did not necessarily imply appropriate sexual identification. Thus, one could conclude that in individual cases, the
speech cues and associated behavior appeared to be verified. However for a number of the assumptions, the total number of postdictions
were numerically too small to be definitive even though they were
suggestive of a relationship. In discussing validating procedures, we
tried to indicate which assumptions were supported by the data,
which assumptions were neither proved nor disproved and which
assumptions were in their present form not highly productive.
Furthermore, postdictions so often were a resultant of multiple cues
that the direct relationship between speech cue and behavior was
sometimes not altogether clear-cut. Clinically, this was advantageous
since it implied balancing and weighing of signs in relation to the
total context of speech patterns. It is for this reason the authors
felt that while in general the major hypothesis concerning meaning-

fulness of speech as an expression of personal style was supported, additional research might extend some of the subsidiary assumptions.

The obtained postdictions were next examined by one of us who had a close knowledge of the children who were involved. An attempt was made to validate the postdictions as substantially correct, incorrect, or inappropriate and unsubstantiated, using as a criterion for judgment principally the prepuberty psychiatric evaluations with occasional reference to other observations, tests, or developmental data.

From a global point of view, the postdictions were highly accurate. Of 233 postdictions made, 193 (83 percent) were judged to be accurate. Eighteen (8 percent) were felt to be inaccurate. Twenty-two (9 percent) were not verifiable from other data. These findings, taken by themselves, support our basic hypothesis that the form and quality of speech is a meaningful dynamic representation of child behavior and that as such, evaluation of speech adds a meaningful dimension to the usual psychological examination.

When the records of individual children were considered, postdictions on 18 (75 percent) of the children proved to be correct more than three-fourths of the time. For an additional five children (21 percent), the level of accuracy varied from 62 percent to 75 percent correct. In one child, postdictions were as often incorrect as correct. (Of ten postdictions made, five were considered incorrect or unsubstantiated by the data.) While we believe that speech may be a highly sensitive index of level of self-esteem and manner of relating to the world, in some individuals positive and negative factors tapped by other forms of psychological evaluations counterbalance the speech signs or indicate distortions in development which are expressed in modes of behavior other than speech.

Bibliography

1. Ballenger, H. C., and Ballenger, J.J.: *Diseases of the Nose, Throat and Ear.* Philadelphia, Lea and Febiger, 1957, pp. 369-370.
2. Bentley, M., and Varon, E. J.: An accessory study of phonetic symbolism, *Am. J. Psychol., 45*:76-86, 1933.
3. Bernier, J. L., and Ash, J. E.: *Atlas of Dental and Oral Pathology.* Washington, Registry Press, 1948.
4. Berry, M. F., and Eisenson, J.: *Speech Disorders: Principles and Practices of Therapy.* New York, Appleton-Century-Crofts, 1956.
5. Blanton, M. G., and Blanton, S.: *Speech Training for Children.* New York, Century, 1920, as cited in Van Riper, C., and Irwin, J.: *Voice and Articulation.* Englewood Cliffs, New Jersey, Prentice-Hall, 1958.
6. Bloomfield, L.: *An Introduction to the Study of Language.* London, Bell, 1914, as cited in Brain, Lord: *Speech Disorders: Aphasia, Apraxia and Agnosia.* Washington, Butterworths, 1961.
7. Boomer, D. S., and Goodrich, D. W.: Speech disturbance and judged anxiety. *J. Consult. Psychol., 24*:160-164, 1961.
8. Brockbill, Y., and Little, K.: Factors determining the guessing of meanings of foreign words. *J. Abn. Soc. Psych., 54*:312-318, 1957.
9. Bradford, L., and Rousey, C.: Psychological Implications of the Whistling S. Unpublished manuscript, 1961.
10. Brain, Lord: *Speech Disorders: Aphasia, Apraxia and Agnosia.* Washington, Butterworths, 1961.
11. Brodbeck, A. J., and Irwin, O. C.: The speech behavior of infants without families. *Child Development, 17*:145-156, 1946.
12. Brody, S.: *Patterns of Mothering.* New York, International Universities, 1956, p. 369.
13. Brown, F. W.: Baby talkers. *Proceedings of American Speech Correction Association, Vol. 6,* 1936, pp. 17-98 and 205-208, as cited in Van Riper, C., and Irwin, J.: *Voice and Articulation.* Englewood Cliffs, New Jersey, Prentice-Hall, 1958.
14. Brown, R., Black, A., and Horowitz, A.: Phonetic symbolism in natural language. *J. Abn. Soc. Psych., 50*:388-393, 1955.

15. Brown, R.: *Words and Things.* Glencoe, Illinois, The Free Press, 1958.

16. Byrne, M.: Personal Communication, 1964.

17. Carrell, J., and Tiffany, W.: *Phonetics: Theory and Application to Speech Improvement.* New York, McGraw-Hill, 1960.

18. Curtis, J. J.: Disorders of Articulation. In *Speech Handicapped School Children,* by Johnson, W., Brown, S., Curtis, J., Edney, C. and Keaster, J. New York, Harper and Brothers, 1956.

19. Davitz, J. R. (Ed.): *The Communication of Emotional Meaning.* New York, McGraw-Hill, 1964.

20. DeLaguna, G. A.: *Speech: Its Function and Development.* New Haven, Yale University Press, 1923, p. 10, as cited in Lillywhite, H.: General concepts of communication. *J. Pediat., 62:*5-10, 1963.

21. Dibner, A. S.: Cue-Counting: A measure of anxiety in interviews. *J. Consult. Psychol., 20:*475-478, 1956.

22. Diedrich, William M.: An Investigation of the Visual Function of Children with Normal Speech and Children with Impaired Articulation. Unpublished doctoral dissertation. Cleveland, Western Reserve University, 1958.

23. Escalona, S., and Leitch, M.: *Early Phases of Personality Development: A Non-Normative Study of Infant Behavior.* Society for Research in Child Development, Monograph No. 17, New Orleans, Louisiana State Univ., 1952.

24. Escalona, Sibylle, and Heider, Grace: *Prediction and Outcome: A Study in Child Development.* Menninger Clinic Monograph Series No. 14. New York, Basic Books, 1959.

25. Escalona, S., and Moriarty, A. E.: Prediction of schoolage intelligence from infant tests. *Child Development, 32:*597-605, 1961.

26. Fairbanks, G.: *Voice and Articulation Drillbook.* 2nd edition. New York, Harper & Brothers, 1960. p. 170.

27. Feldman, S.: *Mannerisms of Speech and Gestures In Everyday Life.* New York, International Universities, 1959.

28. Fletcher, S. G., Casteel, R. L., and Bradley, D. P.: Tongue-thrust swallow, speech articulation and age. *J. Speech Hear. Dis., 26:*201-208, 1961.

29. Fletcher, S.: Personal Communication, 1964.

30. Ford, Frank: *Diseases of the Nervous System in Infancy, Childhood and Adolesence.* 2nd edition. Springfield, Thomas, 1948.

31. Freud, Sigmund (1901): The Psychopathology of Everyday Life. *Standard Edition, 6*:53-105, 1960.
32. Freud, A., and Burlingham, D.: *Infants Wihtout Families*. New York, International Universities, 1944.
33. Freud, Sigmund (1905): Three Essays on the Theory of Sexuality. *Standard Edition, 7*:135-245, 1953.
34. Glauber, I. P.: The Psychoanalysis of Stuttering. In *Stuttering: A Symposium*. J. Eisenson, ed. New York, Harper and Brothers, 1958, pp. 71-120.
35. Gleser, G. C., Gottschalk, L. A., and Springer, K. J.: An Anxiety Scale Applicable to Verbal Samples. *Arch. of Gen. Psychiatry, 5*:593-604, 1961.
36. Goodenough, F.: Anger in Young Children. *Monograph Series No. 9*. Minneapolis, Minnesota, University of Minnesota Press, 1931, as cited in Watson, R.: *Psychology of the Child*. New York, John Wiley and Sons, 1959.
37. Greenson, R. E.: About the sound "MM". *Psa. Quart., 23*:234-239, 1954.
38. Greenson, R.: On the silence and sounds of the analytic hour. *J. Amer. Psa. Assn., 9*:79-84, 1961.
39. Grinker, R. R., and Bucy, P. C.: *Neurology*. Springfield, Thomas, 1949, pp. 40-41.
40. Hartmann, H.: Ego Psychology and the Problem of Adaption. In *Organization and Pathology of Thought*, translated by D. Rapaport. New York, Columbia University Press, 1951, pp. 362-396.
41. Heider, G.: *Vulnerability in Infants and Young Children*, Monograph to be published by Genetic Psychology Monographs.
42. Heinstein, M.: *Behavior Correlates of Breast-Bottle Regimes under Varying Parent-Infant Relationships*. Monograph, Society for Research in Child Development, Vol. 28, #4, Yellow Springs, Ohio, Antioch Press.
43. Henry, J. and Henry, Z.: Speech disturbances in pilaga indian children. *Amer. J. Orthopsychiat., 10*:362-369, 1940.
44. Hirsh, I.: *The Measurement of Hearing*. New York, McGraw-Hill, 1952.
45. Holzman, P.: Personal Communication, 1963.
46. Holzman, P., Rousey, C., Schloesser, H., and Snyder, C.: Personal Communication, 1963.

47. Irwin, J. V.: Psychological Implications of Voice and Articulation Disturbances. In *Psychological Aspects of Speech and Hearing,* D. A. Barbara, ed. Springfield, Thomas, 1960.
48. Irwin, O. C.: Infant speech: vowel and consonant frequency. *J. Speech Dis., 11*:123-125, 1946.
49. Irwin, O. C.: Infant speech: consonantal sounds according to place of articulation. *J. Speech Dis., 12*:397-401, 1947.
50. Irwin, O. C.: Infant speech: development of vowel sounds. *J. Speech Hear., Dis., 13*:31-34, 1948.
51. Jackson C., and Jackson, C. L.: *Diseases of the Nose, Throat and Ear.* Philadelphia, W. B. Saunders, 1946, p. 588.
52. Jakobson, R.: Why Mama and Papa. In *Perspective in Psychological Theory.,* Kaplan, B. and Wapner, S. editors. New York, International Universities Press, 1960, pp. 124-134.
53. Jerger, J.: *Modern Developments In Audiology.* New York, Academic Press, 1963.
54. Jesperson, O.: *Language, Its Nature, Development and Origin.* New York, Henry Holt, 1922, p. 433, as cited in Lillywhite, H.: General concepts of communication. *J. Pediat., 62*:5-10, 1963.
55. Johnson, W., Darley, F., and Spriestersbach, D.: *Diagnostic Methods in Speech Pathology.* New York, Harper and Row, 1962.
56. Kester, B. C.: Some observations on tongue-thrust swallowers. *Amer. J. Orthopsychiat., 33*:284-285, 1963.
57. Klein, G. S., and Schlesinger, H.: Where is the perceiver in perceptual theory? *J. Personality., 18*:32-47, 1949.
58. Krause, M. S.: Anxiety in verbal behavior: intercorrelational study. *J. Consulting Psychol., 25*:272, 1961.
59. Lewis, M. M.: *Infant Speech.* London, Paul Kegan, 1930.
60. Mahl, G. F.: Disturbances and silences in the patient's speech in psychotherapy. *J. Abnorm. Soc. Psychol., 53*:1-15, 1956.
61. Mahl, G. F.: Exploring Emotional States by Content Analysis. In *Trends in Content Analysis.* Urbana, Ill., University of Illinois Press, 1959, pp. 89-130.
62. Mahl, G. F.: Measuring the patient's anxiety during interview from "expressive" aspects of his speech. *Trans. N. Y. Academy of Sciences, 21*:249-257, 1959.
63. Mahl, G. F.: The Expression of Emotions on the Lexical and Linguistic Levels. Paper presented at the meeting of the

American Association for Advancement of Science, New York City, 1960.

64. Maltzman, I., Morrisett, Jr., L., and Brooks, L. O.: *J. Abn. Soc. Psych., 53*:249-251, 1956.

65. Matarazzo, J. D., Hess, H. F., and Saslow, G.: Frequency and duration characteristics of speech and silence behavior during interviews. *J. Clin. Psychol., 18*:416-426, 1962.

66. Mayman, M., and Rousey, C.: Research in process, 1963.

67. McWilliams, B. J.: Psychological implications of consonant sounds. *J. Speech Hear. Dis., 25*:89-91, 1960.

68. Mead, M.: *Male and Female.* New York, William Morrow, 1949.

69. Meringer, R., and Mayer, C.: Versprechen und Verlesen, eine psychologischlinguistische Studie. Vienna, 1895 as cited in Freud, S. (1901): The Psychopathology of Everyday Life. *Standard Edition, 6*:53-105, 1960.

70. Milisen, R., and associates: The Disorder of Articulation: A Systematic Clinical and Experimental Approach. *Monograph Supplement 4, J. Speech Hear. Dis.,* 1954.

71. Miron, M.: A cross-linguistic investigation of phonetic symbolism. *J. Abn. Soc. Psychol., 62*:623-630, 1961.

72. Moore, G. P.: Voice Disorders Associated with Organic Abnormalities. In *Handbook for Speech Pathology,* L. E. Travis, ed., New York, Appleton-Century-Crofts, 1957, pp. 653-706.

73. Moriarty, A. E.: Coping patterns of preschool children in response to intelligence test demands, *Genetic Psychology Monographs, 64,* 3-127, 1961.

74. Moriarty, A. E.: *I. Q. Constancy and I.Q. Change; A Clinical View of Relationships Between Tested Intelligence and Personality.* To be published.

75. Moses, Paul: *The Voice of Neurosis.* New York, Grune and Stratton, 1954.

76. Moyers, R.: The Role of Musculature in Orthodontic Diagnosis and Treatment Planning. In *Vistas In Orthodontics,* edited by Kraus, B. S. & Riedel, R. A., Philadelphia, Lea & Febiger, 1962, pp 309-328.

77. Müller, R. M.: *The Science of Language.* New York, Longmans, Green and Company, 1891, p. 496, as cited in Lillywhite, H.: General concepts of communication. *J. Pediat., 62*:5-10, 1963.

78. Murphy, A.: *Stuttering and Personality Dynamics.* New York, Ronald Press, 1960.

79. Murphy, L. B.: Preventive Implications of Development in the Preschool Years. Chapter 10 in *Prevention of Mental Disorders in Children,* Gerald Caplan, ed. New York, Basic Books, 1961.

80. Murphy, L. B., Moriarty, A. E., and Raine, W.: *Development of Adaptational Styles.* In preparation.

81. Murphy, L. B., and associates: *The Widening World of Childhood. Paths Toward Mastery.* New York, Basic Books, 1962.

82. Nelson, Waldo: *Textbook of Pediatrics.* 7th edition. Philadelphia, W. B. Saunders, 1954.

83. Newby, H.: *Audiology: Principle and Practice.* New York, Appleton-Century-Crofts, 1958.

84. Newman, S. S.: Further experiments in phonetic symbolism. *Am. J. Psychol., 45:*53-75, 1933.

85. Niederland, W. G.: Early auditory experiences, beating fantasies, and primal scene. *Psa. Study of the Child, 13:*471-504, 1958.

86. Nielson, J. M.: Agnosias, Apraxias, Speech and Aphasia. In *Clinical Neurology,* Vol. I, A. B. Barker, ed. New York, Paul B. Hoeber, 1955, pp. 352-378.

87. Orne, M.: The nature of hypnosis: artifact and essence. *J. Abnorm. Soc. Psychol., 58:*277-299, 1959.

88. Orne, M.: On the social psychology of the psychological experiment: with particular reference to demand characteristics and their implications. *Am. Psych., 17:*776-783, 1962.

89. Orton, S. T.: *Reading, Writing and Speech Problems in Children.* New York, W. W. Norton, 1937.

90. Ostwald, P. F.: When people whistle. *Language and Speech, 2:*137-145, 1959.

91. Ostwald, P. F.: Humming, sound and symbol. *J. Auditory Research, 3:*224-232, 1961.

92. Ostwald, P. F.: *Soundmaking: The Acoustic Communication of Emotion.* Springfield, Thomas, 1963.

93. Paget, Sir Richard: *Human Speech.* New York, Harcourt Brace, 1930, Chap. 7, as cited in Lillywhite, H.: General concepts of communication. *J. Pediat., 62:*5-10, 1963.

94. Palmer, J. M.: Tongue thrusting: a clinical hypothesis. *J. Speech Hear. Dis., 27:*323-333, 1962.

95. Pittenger, R. E., and Smith, H. L.: A basis for some contributions of linguistics to psychiatry. *Psychiatry, 20:*61-78, 1957.

96. Pittenger, R. E., Hockett, C. F., and Danehy, J. J.: *The First Five Minutes.* Ithaca, N. Y., Paul Martineau, 1960.

97. Plato: Cratylus. In *The Dialogues of Plato,* translated by B. Jowett, Encyclopedia Britannica, Inc., Chicago, William Benton, 1952, pp. 85-114.

98. Powers, M. H.: Functional Disorders of Articulation: Symptomatology and Etiology. In *Handbook of Speech Pathology,* L. E. Travis, ed. New York, Appleton-Century-Crofts, 1957, pp. 707-768.

99. Provence, S., and Lipton, R. C.: *Infants in Institutions.* New York, International Universities, 1962.

100. Rabban, M.: Sex-role Identification in Young Children in Two Diverse Social Groups. *Genetic Psychology Monograph 42,* 1950, pp. 81-158.

101. Rheingold, H. L.: *The Modification of Social Responsiveness in Institutional Babies.* Monograph of the Society for Research in Child Development, Inc., Vol. 21, No. 2, 1956.

102. Rose, J. A.: Dynamics and treatment of speech disorders. *Amer. J. Orthopsychiat., 13*:284-298, 1943.

103. Rousey, C., and Averill, S.: Speech Disorders Among Delinquent Boys. *Bull. Menninger Clinic, 27*:177-184, 1963.

104. Rousey, C., and Toussieng, P.: Contributions of a Speech Pathologist to the Psychiatric Examination of Children. *Mental Hygiene, 48*:566-575, 1964.

105. Sanford, F.: Speech and personality. *Psychological Bulletin, 39*:811-845, 1942.

106. Sapir, E.: Speech as a personality trait. *Mental Health Bulletin, 5*:1-7 Dec., 1926.

107. Sapir, E.: A study in phonetic symbolism. *J. Exp. Psych., 12*:225-239, 1929.

108. Saporta, S. (editor): *Psycholinguistics.* New York, Holt, Rinehart and Winston, 1961.

109. Schactel, E. G.: *Metamorphosis.* New York, Basic Books, 1959.

110. Scripture, E. W.: *Stuttering, Lisping and Correction of the Speech of the Deaf.* New York, Macmillan, 1923.

111. Searl, N.: Some Emotional Factors Affecting Children's Speech. *Speech,* Vol. 2, 1936, pp. 21-29, as cited in van Riper, C. and Irwin, J.: *Voice and Articulation.* Englewood, N. J., Prentice Hall, 1958.

112. Sears, R. R., Macoby, E. E., and Levin, J.: *Patterns of Child Rearing.* Evanston, Illinois, Row Peterson, 1957.

113. Shoup, J.: Lecture Notes, Vol. II, Engineering Summer Conference

on Automatic Speech Recognition. Summer, 1963, The University of Michigan, Ann Arbor, Michigan.

114. Simon, C. T.: The Development of Speech. In *Handbook of Speech Pathology.* L. E. Travis, ed. New York, Appleton-Century-Crofts, 1957, pp. 3-43.

115. Smith, A.: A Dissertation on the Origin of Language. In *The Theory of Moral Sentiments,* 10th edition. London, Cadell, 1804, p. 343, as cited in Lillywhite, H.: General concepts of communication. *J. Pediat., 62:*5-10, 1963.

116. Solomon, A.: Personality and behavior patterns of children with functional defects of articulation. *Child Dev., 32:*731-738, 1961.

117. Spitz, R.: Hospitalism: An inquiry into the genesis of psychiatric conditions in early childhood. *Psa. Study of the Child, 1:*53-74, 1945.

118. Starkweather, J. A.: Vocal communication of personality and human feelings. *J. Communication, 11:*63-72, 1961.

119. Steer, M. D., and Drexler, H. G.: Predicting later articulation ability from kindergarten tests. *J. Speech Hear. Dis., 25:*391-397, 1960.

120. Stern, C. Undw: Die Kindersprache: tete. Aufl. 1928, as cited by Lewis, M.M.: *Infant Speech.* London, Kegan Paul, 1930.

121. Straub, W. J.: Etiology of the perverted swallowing habit. *Amer. J. Orthodont., 37:*603-610, 1951.

122. Templin, M. C.: *Certain Language Skills in Children.* Monograph No. 26. Minneapolis, University of Minnesota Press, 1957.

123. Templin, M. C., and Darley, F. L.: *The Templin-Darley Tests of Articulation.* Bureau of Educational Research and Services, State University of Iowa, Iowa City, Iowa, 1960.

124. Terman, L. M. and Tyler, L. E.: Psychological Sex Differences. In *Manual of Child Psychology,* L. Carmichael, ed. 2nd edition. New York, John Wiley and Sons, 1954.

125. Thomas, C. K.: *An Introduction to the Phonetics of American English.* New York, Ronald Press Company, 1947.

126. Travis, L. E.: *Speech Pathology.* New York, Appleton-Century-Crofts, 1931.

127. Travis, L. E.: The Unspeakable Feelings of People with Special Reference to Stuttering. In *Handbook of Speech Pathology,* L. E. Travis, ed. New York, Appleton-Century-Crofts, 1957, pp. 916-946.

128. Van Riper, C.: *Speech Correction: Principles and Methods*. 3rd edition. Englewood Cliffs, New Jersey, Prentice-Hall, 1954, p. 187.
129. Van Riper, C., and Irwin, J. V.: *Voice and Articulation*. Englewood Cliffs, New Jersey, Prentice-Hall, 1958, pp. 38-41.
130. Von Herder, J. C. as cited by Müller, F. M.: *The Science of Language*, New York, Longmans, Green and Company, 1891, p. 496. The entire reference cited by Lillywhite, H.: General concepts of communication. *J. Pediat., 62*:5-10, 1963.
131. Watson, R.: *Psychology of the Child*. New York, John Wiley and Sons, 1959.
132. Wechsler, I. S.: *Clinical Neurology*. Philadelphia, W. B. Saunders, 1963, pp. 13-14.
133. Weiss, D.: The Pubertal Change of the Human Voice. *Folia Phoniatrica, Separatum,* Vol. 2, 1950, pp. 126-159.
134. Wepman, J.: *Auditory Discrimination Test: Preliminary Edition*. Private Publication, 950 E. 59th Street, Chicago, 1958.
135. Werner, H.: *Comparative Psychology of Mental Development*. New York, International Universities, 1957.
136. Werner, H.: Grundfragen der Sprachpysiognomik Leipzig, Barth., 1932, as cited in Werner, H. & Kaplan, B.: *Symbol Formation*. New York, John Wiley & Sons, Inc., 1963.
137. Westlake, H.: A system for developing speech with cerebral palsied children. Reprint of 3 articles appearing in August, October and December, 1951 issues of *The Crippled Child,* Chicago, Easter Seal Society.
138. Whitney, W. D.: *Language and the Study of Languages*. New York, Scribner, 1868, p. 429, as cited in Lillywhite H.: General concepts of communication. *J. Pediat., 62*:5-10, 1963.
139. Wilson, S.A.K., and Bruce, A. N.: *Neurology*. Baltimore, Williams and Wilkins, 1955, pp. 880, 902, 1000, 1016, 1151, 1180.
140. Winitz, H.: Personal Communication, 1963.
141. Wundt, G.: Vokerpsychologie, 1, Part 1, Leipzig, 1900 (pp. 60-1-81-131-2), as cited in Freud, Sigmund (1901): The Psychopathology of Everyday Life. *Standard Edition 6*:53-105, 1960.
142. Wundt, W.: *Outlines of Psychology*. 3rd Edition. Leipzig, Kroner, 1907, pp. 339-443, as cited in Lillywhite, H.: General concepts of communication. *J. Pediat., 62*:5-10, 1963.
143. Wyatt, G. L.: Stammering and language learning in early childhood. *J. Abnorm. Soc. Psychol., 44*:75-84, 1949.

144. Wyatt, G. L., and associates: Treatment of stuttering children and their parents: Report of the Wellesley Research Project. A series of papers delivered at the 38th Annual Convention, American Speech and Hearing Association, New York, November, 1962.

INDEX